PAPERS OF A PARIAH

PAPERS OF A PARIAH

BY

ROBERT HUGH BENSON

Essay Index Reprint Series

BOOKS FOR LIBRARIES PRESS, INC.
FREEPORT, NEW YORK

First published 1907
Reprinted 1967

PREFACE

Persons who are good enough to read this book are requested to keep the following setting of it before their minds: —

It was my fortune to meet the author of the following pages in a railway carriage about two years ago, and during the ensuing four months — until, in fact, his death last February year — I may say that I enjoyed his friendship.

His story was, briefly, as follows: —

He had been educated at Rugby and Oxford, and shortly before his father's death a year or two later, finding himself completely alone in the world, he had entered the profession of the stage. Here he was only moderately successful; but he married, in spite of that fact, for he had small private means. Within a year of his marriage his wife died, leaving him once more entirely alone; and he devoted himself again to his art. Before he was forty, however, his health began to suffer; and for the last three years of his life — for he died of consumption at the age of forty-two—he lived alone in a little house on the outskirts of a provincial town whose name I shall take leave to keep to myself.

Here he began, for the first time, apparently, to pay serious attention to the subject of religion, and conformed naturally to that system in which he had been brought up—namely, the Church of England. After one year, however, of this life, he was drawn to enter a Catholic church, and from that time his interest in the Faith never wavered. There was, however, in his constitution a great deal of inchoate agnosticism, and it was not until within a week of his rather unexpected death that I felt myself justified in receiving him into the Catholic Church.

A couple of days later he contracted a serious chill; and it was during visits that I paid to him for the remaining five days of his life on earth, that he spoke to me of a bundle of papers, and committed them to my disposal. It is from those papers that I have made the selection that form the following volume; these, with one exception, have already appeared in the "Month."

As regards their literary merits they must speak for themselves, but as regards their doctrinal position I must take leave to say a word or two.

They were written, it must be remembered, by one who was not only not a Catholic, but who did not at all continuously contemplate the becoming one. Their point of view, therefore — and it is in this, I think, that their interest chiefly lies — is of one who regards the Catholic Church from without, not from within, though with a favourable eye. He was setting himself, though he did not fully realize it at first, to understand rather than to criticize, to hear what the Church had to say for herself through her external system, rather than to dispute her right to speak at all. And it was, I suppose I may say, through his attitude of simplicity, that he merited, so far as one may merit, the grace of conversion.

With some of his thoughts I must confess myself unable to sympathize; his treatment of the "Dance as a Religious Exercise," to mention one among many, appears to me fantastic and impossible, if not bordering, now and

then, on material irreverence; and his phil-
osophy more than once seems to me probably
untenable.

He seems, too, on the most charitable con-
struction, to have been singularly unfortunate
in his acquaintance with Anglican clergy;
and, for myself, I cannot recognize his dic-
tatorial bully and his spiritual hypochondriac
as in any way typical of that fine body of men
among whom I number several friends. He
seems to me to do much less than justice to
the Church of England as a whole.

However, I too do not wish to attack, but to
appreciate; my business is that of an editor,
not of a critic; I have only so far meddled with
his writings as to exclude those that appeared
to me irrelevant or certainly erroneous.

Here it seems to me proper to say a word
or two as to his person and habits.

He was a lean, fair-haired man of about
six feet in height, clean-shaven, slightly bald,
and with the unmistakable actor's face, mobile
and mask-like. He had his disease, I thought,
plainly marked when I first saw him, but in
answer to all entreaties that he would go

abroad or undergo a rigorous treatment, he invariably answered that firstly he was not rich enough, and secondly that he could not be bothered. He seemed to think that he would fulfil his function of life better by continuing his regular habits at home, rather than by exiling himself in an unfamiliar atmosphere, or by bestowing all his attention on getting stout; and I am not sure, after all, that under the circumstances he was to be greatly blamed.

He spent a great deal of his day in the garden, walking up and down the broad path that ran from end to end of it, or reading in his study. He wrote few letters, for he had few friends, but he passed a considerable time each day on his diary, which is also in my possession. In the afternoon he would walk again with his dog, and, towards the end of his life, finish his exercise by a visit to the church. I have myself, two or three times, seen his dog patiently dribbling on the steps during his master's devotions within.

I have no death-bed conversation to record. He died as naturally as he had lived, obviously interested in what was to happen, but

*not impatient; free from any superficial emo-
tion and quite incapable of making what
some might consider suitable remarks. He
received the last sacraments on the morning
of his death, and died at the prosaic hour of
three o'clock in the afternoon.*

*Yet I must confess that I have never
assisted at the passing of a soul with greater
contentment. Our conversations had shown
me how sincere and sound was his faith, his
confessions how deep his penitence. He appeared to me to be an excellent example of
what grace can effect on a perfectly simple soul
which responds to it; which is transformed
without being transfigured; which passes from
the natural to the supernatural without de-
stroying the ladder of its ascent; which is
deliberate without being sluggish, ardent
without fanaticism, poetical without wildness.*

*With regard to the personages mentioned
in his pages, I need hardly say that I have
changed their names, and that Father Thorpe
is not myself.*

Robert Hugh Benson.

November, 1906.

CONTENTS

PAPERS OF A PARIAH

AT A REQUIEM

November, 1903.

THIS morning I assisted at one of the most impressive dramas in the world — I mean the Solemn Requiem Mass celebrated by the Catholic Church on All Souls' Day.

It was sung in a beautiful church, of which the altar, the steps, and the reredos were draped in black. In the centre of the choir stood a great catafalque, shaped like a gigantic coffin, yellow and black on a black carpet: six candlesticks as high as a man held each a burning yellow candle. There were three priests at the altar, two of them attached to the church, and the third, who acted as deacon, appeared to be a monk, for his amice-veiled hood hung over his shoulders. There was a small

1

choir of boys who sang very sweetly, and
one man who sang alone, for no organ was
used, endless and sombre melodies from a
great book on a lectern. It was a very
dark morning without and within, and the
immense slender columns of the church
soared up into a gloom that might well be
thronged with watching souls. Beneath,
perhaps a hundred persons (mostly in black
clothes), half of whom were children, stood
and knelt and sat without a sound for nearly
an hour.

I am quite aware that many regard such a
ceremony as idle and useless, if not worse;
but they do so from a dogmatic standpoint,
and I am not concerned with that now.
It is as a representation of death and all
that that means that I think it worth de-
scribing: for it is to be seriously doubted
whether any other religion under the sun
gives so adequate and moving a picture of
the one eternal tragedy which so far as is
possible darkens the light of that sun for
us all.

The Church makes no exceptions or

concessions in the case of her children who have died in the odour of sanctity: all have fallen short, she declares, and need the mercy of their God. As for the departed souls considered as a body on this day, so for each separate soul that dies in her communion, she prescribes penitence, mourning, and petition. There is no attempt to canonize before the time; no desperate effort after brightness or triumph. White flowers and wreaths of laurel remain still unrecognized in her ritual. It is the same for all, black and smoky yellow, and black again, and, through all, melancholy melodies that wail and soar as if souls indeed were crying from a pit wherein is no water. There is hope, certainly; but not a touch of exultation, for the time for that is not yet come.

Yet her faith and charity are unbounded. In her calendar is set down the words, *In die omnium defunctorum*, without exception or qualifying clause; and in her sanctuary is reared up a catafalque, empty of a material coffin, but crowded, to her mystical

eyes, with a multitude which no man can
number of souls forgotten and remembered
that hasten here to take refuge under a pall
as ample as her love and as heavy as death.
Round this emblem of dead humanity there
is raised a wall of fire, signified by the six
flames rising from yellow wax, as if to keep
off the darkness of the grave; and about it
go her priests, sprinkling hallowed water to
cleanse corruption, and drowning with sad-
smelling, fragrant incense the odour that
not even she can wholly obliterate.

It is she again who, while eternally young
and undying, identifies herself with the
myriads of the dead, gathering them all
up in her own person.   As she looks forward with terrified eyes to the great day
which she proclaims is at hand, she cries
out in fear, uniting with herself all who will
need mercy then.

> *Quid sum miser tunc dicturus ?*
> *Quem patronum rogaturus ?*
> *Cum vix justus sit securus ?*

And again as she looks back to that from
which springs her hope:

Recordare, Jesu pie,
Quod sum causa tuae viae;
Ne me perdas illa die. . . .
Qui Mariam absolvisti,
Et latronem exaudisti,
Mihi quoque spem dedisti.

Then once more she turns on herself, comes back to the present, and while still on earth, prays for those who are not, as a mother might pray for absent children.

Eternal rest give unto them, O Lord: And let light perpetual shine upon them. . . .

Then, as if in a piteous struggle against her own stern creed which declares that eternal destinies are decided at death, she entreats God to deliver the souls of her departed children from the gates of hell: and once more, remembering the Day that is always before her eyes, "Deliver me, Lord," she cries through the mouth of her priest, "from eternal death in that tremendous day: when heaven and earth are moved, while Thou comest to judge the earth through fire. I am all trembling and afraid, while judgment comes and wrath approaches. . . ." "May they rest in peace. Amen."

"Never in any religion," writes a French author, "has a more charitable part, a more august mission, been assigned to man. Lifted by his consecration wholly above humanity, almost deified by the sacerdotal office, the priest, while earth laments or is silent, can advance to the brink of the abyss and intercede. . . . Timid and distant, plaintive and sweet, this *Amen* said, 'We have done what we could, but . . . but . . .'"

Now all this may appear dangerous nonsense to many people; but, as I said before, I am not concerned with dogma. It was as a mirror of my own human instincts and ideas that this Mass for the Dead moved me so profoundly. Whether or not that sacrifice and those prayers prevail, the whole affair was none the less an amazing drama as true to life as to death.

Death is an exceedingly unpleasant fact, but it is a fact; and, I suppose, that there never has lived a man who has not formed some ideas on the subject. There is first of all its horror and darkness; and it is not the smallest use to pretend that we are not aware of these features. The Gospel of Cheerfulness, preached so gaily and courageously by Stevenson, and welcomed so thankfully by many thousands of readers, is a poor thing if it does not take into account the end of us all. Of course the perfection of philosophy is to unite all known data into a single theory; but for most of us it is necessary to go into committee on life, and consider its component elements one by one; we have not attained to the serene heights of eternal contemplation. While we regard the phenomenon of Birth it is not possible to do justice to that of Death — the cradle and the grave are too far apart to be included in one glance — no more than at marriage a man should set about engaging his counsel for the Divorce Court.

Therefore it is surely wholesome for us now and then, though not too often, to look steadily upon coffins and churchyards. To dwell always in a nuptial chamber or a dining-room is as narrow and enervating,

as it is morbid and depressing to pitch our
tents permanently in a cemetery. Nor is
it even the highest philosophy to level the
graves to a lawn and plant flowers there,
and turn a stream through it, and pretend
that it is something else. It is not something else; it is a cemetery.

Now this element of death is perfectly
recognized at a Requiem. I despair of
making clear, to those who cannot see it
for themselves, the indescribably terrible
combination of the colours of yellow and
black, the deathliness of the contrast between flames and the unbleached wax from
which they rise. No man could come
away from a Requiem Mass, where he had
behaved with a decent mental composure,
without being aware, both from the sights
he has looked upon, and the sounds that he
has heard — those wailing airs unsupported
by the genial organ, those clusters of neumes
that rise and falter as they rise — without
being aware that Death is a terrible and a
revolting thing: I defy him to be eloquent
in the bleak Gospel of Cheerfulness for at

least ten minutes after the last *Amen* has
ceased.

This then is faced; but it is not left there.
Other emotions have been represented, and
chief among them that emotion of hope
that so resolutely refuses to die. A man
may laugh at Purgatory, and proclaim in
debating societies that he for one regards
himself as a candle that will presently be
blown out; but when he is quite alone and
has drunk his glass of whisky-and-water,
and thrown the butt of his cigarette into
the fire, and the last doors have banged,
and he gets up and whistles himself into his
bedroom — well, I venture to assert that
he would not have drunk his glass so
genially or whistled so shrilly, if he was not
perfectly aware that somewhere below that
beautiful waistcoat there was a dim and
faint hope that he had over-stated the case
just now in Jones' rooms.

That emotion, then — quite apart from
explicit statements of dogma — has been
represented in the Requiem Mass. Else
why the smell of incense, the beads of water,

and the candle-flames? It is very well to
speak of the "Confraternity of the Faithless
. . . where, on an altar, on which no taper
burned, a priest, in whose heart peace had
no dwelling, might celebrate with unblessed
bread and a chalice empty of wine," but
after all, when such a sanctuary is raised,
I predict that some one of the Confraternity,
no doubt with many apologies and dis-
claimers, will be found to insist upon
striking a match. Men can no more live
without fire and light than hearts can continue to beat without hope.

And these two emotions, terror and hope,
are welded into a trinity by a third that
partakes of the nature of both, — I mean
penitence.

We are all perfectly at liberty to dislike
that word; it is possible that we associate
it with hypocrisy, or weak-mindedness, or
crocodile-crying; but we know what is
meant by it; and surely it may stand as a
label upon that piece of luggage that we
all bear with us, and which contains in
its paradoxical constitution regret for an

irrevocable past, and a certainty that it is
neither past nor irrevocable. Charity, Mr.
Chesterton says somewhere, is the pardon-
ing of the unpardonable; and may we not
add to that, that penitence is a denying of
the undeniable?

This emotion too, then, is well represented in a Requiem; in fact we may say
that nothing else is represented except so
far as it is an element of this. From the
Confiteor Deo omnipotenti of the three black
and white figures bowed at the foot of the
altar to the last doubtful *Amen*, the whole
performance is nothing else than one heart-
broken sob of sorrow. It is possible that we
may repudiate the theological idea of sin;
but we cannot help allowing (what comes
to pretty well the same thing) that there are
certain events in our own lives and in the
lives of other people, that we regret extremely, certain failures to achieve the
right thing, certain achievements which we
should prefer to have failed.

And I suppose, too, that when that unpleasant fact to which a Requiem witnesses

becomes quite imminent, we shall experience that regret even more acutely; at any rate, it would not be unreasonable to do so.

Very well, then; it is exactly that in which Mass for the Dead rises head and shoulders above any other form of funeral devotion. The Catholic Church does not emulate the eminent man who, when requested by his weeping friend at the hour of death to declare what was it that gave such a supernatural radiance to his face, answered with a patient smile that it was "the memory of a long and well-spent life." On the contrary, she makes not one reference to the virtues of the deceased — though it is only just to say that she has done that the day before — she does not recount victories, or even apologize for failures; she does what she considers even better, she deplores them.

The conclusion of the whole matter then is that I am pleased to have gone through those exercises on All Souls' Day, because I feel that they have been extremely good

for me. I do not need any reminders that
I am alive, nor that immortality may be
only a brilliant guess, nor that I am an
exceedingly fine, manly, successful, and
capable person. But it is not bad for me
to be told silently, in a very vivid and impressive manner, that I am certainly going
to die some day, that hope is a fact that
must be accounted for, and that, in spite of
my singular probity and extraordinary gifts,
there are just a few incidents here and
there in my long roll of triumphs for which
I should like to be sorry.

ON THE DULNESS OF
IRRELIGIOUS PEOPLE

DECEMBER, 1906.

I HAVE, wreathed in smiles, this moment let out of my front door a second cousin of mine who has done me the honour of paying his respects at my poor house within a week of his arrival in the town; and I must acknowledge that my geniality arose rather from the prospect of his departure than from the retrospect of his visit. I think I have seldom been so much bored; and yet he is a perfectly intelligent man, he converses agreeably, and he listens as much as he talks. And now that I am alone once more, I feel impelled to discuss the mystery of his abysmal dreariness.

In a word, I believe that it arises from his lack of the religious sense.

Now, we have not been talking about
14

religion (nor even about art, which I hold
to be a kind of religion in solution); in fact,
I seldom wish to engage in conversation
about God; I am sufficiently occupied with
thinking about Him. Religion is one of
those matters on which my judgment is so
entirely in a state of suspense that conversation on the subject can be no more than a
weighing of contrary opinions. It is, so to
speak, *sub judice*, and the judge's mouth is
consequently sealed. I am no controver-
sialist; I wish neither to give nor receive
blows in this quarrel; I have no interest in
dogma beyond the question as to whether
it may not happen to be true, and I know
that George has no contribution to offer
on that point. He has not arrived at the
question as to whether it is true, for he has
already pronounced sentence to the effect
that it cannot possibly be anything but
false, and therefore is no more worth his
discussing than if a Sadducee should take
sides in a scholastic disputation as to the
number of angels capable of dancing simultaneously on the point of a pin.

I am not, therefore, piqued by his silence; on the contrary, I appreciate his kindness; my distress is caused rather by my contemplation of that arid waste which he calls his mind.

Now, it is full of facts intelligently selected and arranged; he has a pretty taste in domestic architecture; the land where he dwells flows with the milk of human kindness and the honey of friendly affection; but what is the matter with it is that it is not a Land of Promise. There is nothing whatever beyond; no glimpse of cloud-wreathed mountains, no peep of a flushed sky, no song of hidden birds, no whisper of a wind that comes whence no man knows and goes whither no man guesses. It is not even shrouded in gloom from which a trumpet of wrath one day might blow; there is no peak where God's feet might stand when He comes to shake the earth; no smoke to hint of hidden powers that one night may burst in fire. It is like such a landscape as you might see in a commercial traveller's dream of Paradise.

It has paved streets, admirably drained,
lines of houses planned on the most modern
system, and, beyond, the eye of the dreamer
descries a flat plain, watered by a straight
river on whose bosom are borne, not gallant
ships with poop and gilding, but sensible
barges, loaded to the water's edge with the
necessaries of life. The fields stand thick
with corn, but of such a character that no
man is moved to laugh or sing: his sheep
bring forth thousands and ten thousands,
but not in the streets, for that would
interfere with the traffic; his sons grow
up like the young plants, but they are
trained properly against the walls: his
daughters cannot be compared to polished
corners of the temple, for George would
not know a temple by sight if he saw
one: he would think it to be a Corn-
Exchange.

Place by this the mind, let us say, of a
dancing dervish or a Welsh revivalist; and
what refreshment is there! The houses are
ill-planned, the manure-heap it may be
drains into them, as in many an Irish

village; the children are dirty and stand
with tangled hair in eyes and fingers in
mouth; there is no economy, no thrift, no
organization of resources; there is nothing
that spells even the initial letter of Progress; there is not a grain of commonsense
to be found in the dilapidated barns; and
yet I could spend my life here and not
there, for love of the laughter, the tears,
the mystery and the hope. For the sky
is heavy with rain-clouds and gashed with
blue; the wind blows your hat off, it may
be, but it stirs also the dew on the hedges
and lifts the long grass; there is mud under-
foot, but there may be jewels there too,
or a button perhaps, or a fragment of a
chandelier, or a tin soldier, or an ancient
boot. There are mountains behind where
saints may walk, or elves dance, where
the deer live and the goats and strange wild
creatures that fly at the sight or scent of
man. The tangled string of water that
desires you to mistake it for a stream,
would bear no barge, it would not turn
even a mill-wheel; but it is sufficient to

sweep paper boats down sideways, to make
music in the night, to tell you of the far-off
marshes whence it drew its life, and of the
sea that will be its transfiguration and its
tomb.

But the matter becomes the death of the
doubly-slain when we turn from George's
outlook to the prospect seen from a Catholic's window.

Observe, if you please, first the winding
street beneath, ill-paved, perhaps, but then
it was laid down nineteen centuries ago.
There are no side-walks; but is not the
jostle of peasant and prince, of apple-
woman's cart and beauty's litter, of mangy
donkey and knight's steel-clad charger,
surprisingly pleasant? Would you seri-
·ously change that for a boulevard with
electric trams and limes wrapped up in rail-
ings? Not that this city has no open spaces;
for see far down there, beyond the swinging
signs and the toppling houses, the great
market-square where the images of the
saints are sold, and cabbages, and fish for
Friday, and lentils for Ash Wednesday,

and all the rest of the dear, evil-smelling
truck. There are blows bartered there
sometimes, as well as onions and pence,
and knives flash out, and little streaks of
heart's blood run between the cobbles; but
after all, is that so much worse than a
solemn-faced policeman and Black Maria
and the dispassionate hanging of a frantic
man? Look across, too, into that window
opposite, scarce a yard away; the diamond
panes are thick with dust, but how pleasing
is the glow of the wood-fire within, and the
dim lines of the carved bed, and the grotesque shadow of the old man sitting over
his beans in the chimney-corner. Would
you prefer lace-curtains and a geranium-pot?

See that very date and a pair of initials
cut in the oak beneath your elbow, scratched
three centuries ago perhaps by a lover with
a string of beads in one hand and a knife
in the other, lust, I dare say, in his heart,
but a scapular above it that may save him
yet. Is that not better than a foul word
scribbled on a paling, that all deplore and
none remove?

Look at that tawdry image at the street-
corner with a little lamp before it and a
faded marigold at its foot. Would you
take that down and erect instead a marble
image in frock-coat and trousers of a man
who had side-whiskers and a blameless life
to his credit, and a heart of flesh instead of
fire, and eyes that looked upon a bank-
ing-book instead of upon God, to his last-
ing and eternal shame? I tell you that
George's town is full of such; and I think
that he would invoke them every morning
if he had sufficient imagination and no one
was looking.

And now for the supreme sight of this
amazing city. Look up there to the right
and see those monstrous masses, those flying
arches, those incredible pinnacles soaring
against a sky of pearl and amber. Have
you ever seen a sight like that? Look well
at it; for some say it is too good to be true;
it will crumble when the sun sets; it is an
illusion of clouds. (But, for my part, I prefer
to think that it is too good not to be true;
though I would not bias you for the world.)

Within that long wall pierced by windows
it is said that strange men dwell in white
habits, with downcast faces and a measured
walk. Wonderful things are whispered of
them on Saturday nights round the fire; it
is reported that they talk with angels, that
they have found the key to the kingdom of
Heaven, which, if what one said long ago is
true, is to be found in your heart and mine,
if we knew but the secret of its unlocking.
There at least they are said to dwell; it is at
least from that direction that they come
walking sometimes, and up that street that
they return. But none that I know have
been with them; the air is too keen up those
thousand steps, the sounds of warring clouds
too awful, the faces that look from the
windows on either side too white for you
or me.

But this at least is certain — the Lord
of the city dwells in that castle beneath;
for he comes down here sometimes, riding
on a white mule, himself in white and red,
waving signs and smiling on the crowds
that kneel on this side and that. I do

not know if what they say of him is true —
that he is more than just an old man with
a kindly face and a white cap; that he has
treasures of which the world does not
dream, that at his nod angels fall to pray-
ing, and when he speaks there is commo-
tion in the clouds. It may be false; there
may be no angels, or clouds, or treasures;
but what must it be to lean always from
this window and believe every word of it
as he comes riding past to the jingle of bells
and the waving of fans and the crying of
the crowd!

Here is a city of bells; the sun is near
its setting, and from the huge tower of the
Lord's castle sound three strokes and cease;
and in a moment all the world stands still.
Across these broad planes of golden light
above the roofs and the twisted chimneys
come sounding a myriad answers; from
chapel and church and nunnery and guild-
hall. But these fantastic folk beneath us,
suddenly petrified, stand silent with moving
lips. The Lord himself up there has risen
from his supper-table and laid down his

fork; the mule-driver ceases to curse and
rests his hand on his beast's shoulder; the
old man has set down his beans; the mother
pauses in her rocking of the cradle, and
looks at the crying child as if she did not
hear him.

Is it then a fire-alarm, or the warning
of a troop coming up from the sea, or the
signal for a massacre? I can tell you that
it is none of these; but what it is I scarcely
understand; nor scarcely believe what has
been told me. You must ask another.
It concerns a maiden and a child and an
angel — no more than that. . . .

Now is not this wild stuff? For I am
back again in my room alone; and the
dottel of George's pipe has hardly ceased to
smoke in the fender; and the candles are
not burned down half an inch since he left
me. But I have no question as to where
I would sooner dwell — whether in George's
boulevards, or in Mosque Al Aksar, or in
the City of dreams, where some of my
friends insist that life can be supported.

I am not concerned at this moment as to whether this or that is true, for I have no means of telling; perhaps some day I may see more clearly. This only I know; that it is better to hope than to despair, it is better to be doubtful than positive, it is better to open doors than to shut them; it is better to affirm than to deny, to believe the best rather than the worst. And lastly this, that if to live means to be like my second cousin, — it is far, far better to die than to live. . . .

INTELLECTUAL SLAVERY

JANUARY, 1904.

OUR new curate called upon me the other day and remained to tea; in fact, he remained till seven o'clock; and I cannot but suspect that he gave me so much of his time by reason of a rumour which has run through the parish, like sparks through stubble, to the effect that I was observed coming out of the Papistical Massing-house last Friday, about four o'clock in the afternoon. Mr. Joliffe's cart, with its blue-smocked, blood-stained driver, was certainly drawn up opposite Miss Simpson's house about that hour, and I suspect that her maid's attention was drawn to my emerging figure: probably when she took up the buttered toast her mistress was informed, — and no more explanation is needed.

My young spiritual pastor pronounced a

very fervent discourse upon intellectual
slavery, placing his fingers together and
looking tactfully into the fire for fear that
he should observe my confusion. He
pressed my hand sympathetically, too, as
he took his leave, looking sweetly into my
eyes meanwhile, with the air of one who
says, "I understand; I understand. But
take courage and be resolute."

I of course was silent in the presence of
an ordained clergyman; for I have long
since learned that nothing is to be gained
by speech on such occasions. My poor
little earthen pot of theology cannot swim
for an instant in the same stream with a
brazen vessel hammered with consummate
craftsmanship for three long years in St.
Catherine's College at Cambridge, put
through the fire of St. Paul's Epistles in
the original Greek once more in Birming-
ham Theological Seminary for eighteen
months, polished and brought to perfection
by four years' intellectual struggle with the
villagers of Little Brasted, and the occasional reading of Dr. Pearson's standard

work upon the Creed. Besides, I have noticed that ecclesiastics of the Establishment are seldom able to keep the personal note out of religious discussion: they are apt to beg one, as it were a kind of return-call, to come to church for Morning Prayer, and to take as an insult to their personal erudition and authority any questioning of their tenets. I must confess that I prefer to be told by a Papist cleric that he does not care a twopenny piece whether I believe him or not — (and I generally don't believe him and tell him so) — but that I shall certainly be damned if I do not; and meanwhile (since nothing is to be gained by anticipating the Judgment Day and our final severance), will I have another glass of whisky and water?

But the Rev. Mr. Marjoribanks' remarks have set me thinking; and I am determined to pour out my baffled spleen on paper, and behind his back, since I am not man enough to do it in his presence.

I understood him to say that the Popish

Church fetters the intellect; that free thought and free speech are forbidden; that the souls in bondage to that institution walk in chains with the task-master's whip flickering about their shoulders; in short — well, all the rest of it.

Now, what do we mean by "liberty"? It appears to me more pertinent to deal with that question first.

A lion is at liberty who can follow the laws of his own nature, who can eat when his stomach tells him, who can sleep when his fierce eyes grow weary, who can scratch long furrows in a forest tree when his claws feel so disposed. He is not at liberty when he lives in a cage, is fed on horseflesh at 4 p.m., and is compelled at the point of a red-hot poker to spell P-I-G — PIG, in the presence of a diverted crowd.

According to Mr. Marjoribanks a Papist resembles a lion, or rather a kind of fox or jackal, in the latter circumstances; he is caged in Councils and infallible pronouncements, he is told when and where to obtain grace, and he is prodded by a weapon which his own superstitious fears and the ambitions of his clergy have heated red-hot in the fire of a bogus hell.   While Mr. Marjoribanks resembles the monarch of beasts at liberty, ranging this fair world at his own will, choosing this doctrine and not that for his sustenance, resting under the shadow of whatever institution seems the more convenient — which in his case happens to be the Church of England — tearing down this monstrous figment and sparing that tender plant, the terror of agnostics and the envy and admiration of a captive Christendom.

But let us push the analogy further up the scale, and make a comparison more befitting the gentleman's condition.   Let us imagine, not a lion, but a child; and ask ourselves, which has the more liberty, the child who has mastered the laws of grammar, the elements of history and geography, and a few of the physical facts that tend to make life more easy (such as that fire burns, pins prick, gunpowder explodes in the eyes if ignited immediately below them, and that the consumption of yew-berries leads to internal discomfort) — or the child who ranges the forest with the hungry lion looking at him out of a bush, who picks up a red-hot brand because it looks pretty, whose vocabulary is confined to the monosyllables "boo" and "bah," who thinks that a hedgehog will be an agreeable bed-fellow.

Now really, Mr. Marjoribanks, the civilized child has the advantage in point of liberty. It is true that his liberty came under a disguise, when it compelled him to sit at a table with Mademoiselle from ten to twelve and six to seven, but he sat there for the purpose of having chains broken, not forged. He was being freed, for example, from the belief that Bagdad could be reached in a day's journey, and from the discomforts of an attempt that he might otherwise have made to find it; he was being freed from the painful experience of picking up a red-hot coal; from the narrowing view that the sounds that Frenchmen make to one another are nothing but unmeaning grunts and whines; and from the potentiality of pain that lay hidden in those attractive red berries.

In other words, information, if true, makes for freedom, not slavery.

If we turn to the laws that govern society we are confronted by a similar fact. I am more free in that I can walk abroad in Little Brasted with no other weapon than an umbrella, than if my safety could only be found in a suit of steel, a vizored helmet, and a battleaxe; and the reason of my freedom is to be sought ultimately in the presence of a policeman, the existence of the gallows, and all the other sanctions of justice against which the Anarchists cry so lamentably. Discipline, therefore, and the threat of penalties, do not necessarily enslave their subjects, and the only question I have a right to put is not, Is not this compulsion, and therefore slavery? but, Do these regulations tend to the conservation of society and to the survival of the individual under conditions where he may follow out the laws of normal life?

Let us, therefore, apply these analogies

to the doctrine and discipline of the Christian religion.

When the Papist informs me that God is in the tabernacle with the Body, Blood, and Human Soul assumed in the Incarnation, it is the merest folly to answer, "Such information fetters my freedom of thought, for it deprives me, if I believe it, of the liberty of thinking that He is not there." When he tells me that I have to choose between going to Mass and going to Hell, and that an impure thought deliberately entertained places me in hostility to God Almighty, who has bidden me to be pure in heart if I wish to enjoy the Beatific Vision, it is simple stupidity for me to answer, "You should not have told me these truths, for by doing so you have deprived me of the liberty of remaining in bed all Sunday morning, and of encouraging the luxury of a foul imagination." For information, if it is true, does not enslave a man, but rather frees him from the fetters of ignoring it, as well as of the painful consequences of disregarding it.

If, then, the Papist is right, my liberty is

increased, not lessened, by the fact that I know more than I did before. Ignorance may be bliss, but it certainly is not freedom, except in the minds of those who prefer darkness to light, and chains to liberty. The more true information we can acquire, the better for our enfranchisement.

Push the parallel back once more into the physical sphere, and re-tread the ground from another direction. Granted the existence of God the Creator, it is evident that the laws of nature are one expression of His will. I may or may not like those laws; they may appear to me indeed profoundly arbitrary; but it is better that I should know them than be ignorant of them, for it is only by the knowledge of them that I have any hope of gaining the mastery of them for my own use, or indeed of surviving at all on earth. To be ignorant of the properties of lightning and to take my stand during a thunderstorm on the top of a high hill, brandishing a steel rod in either hand, is to court the disaster by which Ajax fell. The scientist, therefore, who informs my ignorance, and explains to me how electric force may be not only evaded but positively set to turn the wheels of my motor-brougham, cannot justly be cried out upon as a tyrant over my thoughts or a subverter of my liberty.

Even Mr. Marjoribanks, I imagine, would grant me this; and therefore I should desire, if I had the courage, to direct his attention to the parallel line in the spiritual world. Presumably God Almighty has a system of government, enactments, rewards, and penalties for that world as for this. An expert therefore in that realm, when he discloses to me the secrets of God's will, cannot be blamed if my personal predilections happen to conflict with theological facts. I may not like going to confession, any more than I like the destructive energy of lightning, or the astringent properties of quinine, but if those things are facts I had better know them.

Ah! Mr. Marjoribanks, I see you writhing on your chair with the pangs of refutation.

"That is all very well: but God is not in the tabernacle, any more than in the confessional: you need not, in fact you must not, go to Mass, for it is no less than idolatry. Therefore, when the Papist tells you this or that, he is enslaving you after all, darkening your intellect with fallacies, and inflaming your imagination with delusions."

Ah! sir, I understand. But observe how you have shifted your platform. When you sat in my chair just now you made as if you waived the question as to whether the Papist religion were true or not; you set that generously on one side as irrelevant; and you were content to point out to me that, true or not, such a system, mapping out as it does the *minutiae* of what is to be believed or practised, could not but exercise an enslaving influence on the fair liberty of thought with which God had endowed me. But if this is all that you mean, I agree with you most heartily. The vital question for us both is not, Should we prefer to have a minute revelation, to be experts in the

Divine Will? — but, Is the Romish claim to give me such a revelation justified or not by fact?

It is to that question that I had been endeavouring to set my poor powers to work, when the butcher remarked me on the steps of St. Aloysius' Church. . . .

A FATHER IN GOD

MARCH, 1904.

IT is a very common accusation against the Catholic clergy that they lord it over God's inheritance, that they are domineering and peremptory; and I suppose it must be confessed that not only is such a charge occasionally true of individuals, but that it corresponds with some characteristic of that body as a whole; for this accusation is levelled, not only by the enemies of the Church, but even now and then by her own fractious children.

Now, I have lately had one or two opportunities for observing the bearing of the priest in this town, and as neither an enemy nor an adherent, but a moderately intelligent spectator, I cannot help feeling that I have witnessed a display of that characteristic temper, but that I am forced to

38

interpret it not adversely but almost favourably. More than once I certainly noticed a brusque peremptoriness, but I am inclined to think that, so far as it was unfortunate, it arose not from a defect but an advantage.

For example, last Thursday I was taking tea with Father Thorpe; and as soon as he had finished he lit a cigarette. But he had not drawn more than a couple of whiffs before his rather slovenly maid came in to announce that Mrs. Johnson wished to see him. He nodded without saying anything, and went blandly on with his cigarette and his conversation. After about five minutes he ground out the red tobacco on to his saucer, finished his sentence in a very leisurely manner, rapped his fingers a little on the table, and asked me to excuse him a moment. He went into the next room, leaving the door half open behind him; and I am bound to say that unintentionally I caught a scrap or two of the conversation.

Now, Mrs. Johnson is, as I happen to

know, about the most wealthy Catholic in
this little provincial town; and she is not
at all the kind of woman who would bear
domineering from even an archangel.   She
is a large, severe creature, full, I should
suppose, of self-regard, and certainly very
capable in her way: and she is wealthy, I
say, from our suburban standpoint; by
which I mean that when she dines with the
banker she drives both to and from his
residence in a closed fly.

I could not hear what she said; and at
first I could not hear what the priest said;
then at last his voice sounded clear and
distinct and slightly peevish.

"My dear child, don't talk such nonsense."

I must confess that I smiled all over my
face. Mrs. Johnson's age, I should suppose,
is thirty-seven, and Father Thorpe's cannot
be more than forty-one.   Father Thorpe is
a poor man; Mrs. Johnson is a rich woman.
Yet the man called the woman a "child,"
and bade her not talk nonsense.

There was a little more murmuring of voices; then I heard a rustle of silk and the woman's voice, bland and grateful.

"Very well, Father, if you think so."

"I'll go and see him soon," said the priest, "and there must be an end of it. You understand, don't you?"

Then in two minutes he was back again, and we went on talking as if nothing was the matter.

Now, I do not say that his keeping the lady waiting while he finished his cigarette, nor his cavalier treatment of what was probably a complaint of some sort, were either courteous or apostolic actions; but I do hold, from other things that I have noticed as regards his relations with his flock, that they sprang from a state of affairs that ought to be the envy of the rest of Christendom. A Catholic priest is more than a mere father in name; he is really and truly a parent to his people; he is human and peevish sometimes, like the rest of us; he is thoughtless occasionally, no doubt, and selfish, and brusque; but, when all is said and done, he is not in the least like a lawyer, who must be polite if he wishes to retain his clients, or a tradesman, who must be prompt and subservient if he desires to sell his wares. On the contrary, he is regarded, as I have said, as a father who has his moods like any one else, but who remains a father and retains his rights in spite of occasional shortcomings; he has authority to scold, as well as to forgive sins, and to say (sometimes quite unreasonably) that his word must be final, as well as to declare the counsel of God.

To this I know it may be plausibly answered that he has won this position by fear; that, since he is supposed to hold the keys of Heaven he is of course a dangerous man to quarrel with, and that the instance I have quoted is simply one more example of detestable priestcraft.

Yet the retort to that is perfectly easy, and falls under two heads, the general and the particular.

As regards the general principle, I can only assure my fellow-Protestants that no priest could ever deny the sacraments or pretend to withhold grace of any sort from those who happened to be personally rude to him. If Mrs. Johnson had flounced out of the room and told her pastor to hold his tongue or mend his manners, nothing in the world would have happened, except perhaps an extreme astonishment and a possible loss of temper on the part of Father Thorpe. There would have been no bell, book, or candle rung, read, or extinguished on the following Sunday to the chastisement of Mrs. Johnson's soul.

And, as regards the particular instance under our attention, I can only say that to see, as I have seen, Father Thorpe in his school playground, is coincident with dismissing from the mind any suspicion that that clergyman rules by fear.

No: the solution lies a great deal deeper than that; it is to be found in the whole conception that the Catholic laity have formed of the functions of their pastor.

First, of course, since he is a priest he
must be implicity obeyed and believed in
the comparatively small sphere of faith
and morals, though this does not involve
the impossibility of appealing from him to
his superior when his subject is in grave
doubt. This power of appeal, however, is
practically never exercised, owing to the
admirable training and searching examina-
tions through which every priest must
pass — in these deep matters the priest
knows his business, which is to declare
not his original views, but the Faith of
his Church.

But, secondly, since he is a real father
to his flock, his influence, although only
that of a fallible man, covers a very wide
field. His boys will consult him as to their
prospects of work; his girls will ask his
advice as to their dealings with trouble-
some suitors. Often he may give faulty
counsel, for he is acting in these things as
an individual, not as a representative of
Ecclesia Docens; but nevertheless that
counsel is frequently sought and generally

followed. Even when he is not consulted
he occasionally intervenes, as when an Irish
priest in Liverpool issues forth on Saturday
nights with a hunting-crop kept for that
purpose in his passage, to disperse a howling mob of his excited children who are
paying the wrong sort of attention to the
officer of the Saxon law.

Now, I do not deny that this extraordinary influence is occasionally abused,
and that priests, since they are human, will
sometimes interfere where they ought not;
but the danger is inseparable from every
position of authority. Home-life is continually marred by the efforts or selfish-
ness of a domineering father; yet few will
be found to deplore paternal correction in
general on account of these particular draw-
backs; and, with regard to the Catholic
priesthood, it may be asserted without
doubt that for every one such over-stepping
of the limits there can be quoted ten thousand instances where a mistake is avoided
or a catastrophe averted because there was
such a man in the presbytery who could

be consulted without timidity and obeyed
without question.

Does not such a man, after all, exactly
meet a need that can hardly be met otherwise? Discretion and acquaintance with
human nature have been worked into his
very fibre through his studies in casuistry
and his practice in the confessional: he has
a knowledge of family life beyond that of
most married persons, and this knowledge
is impregnated with kindliness, not bitter-
ness; he is sufficiently impressive to command confidence; he is indulgent through
his very experience of weakness and sin;
and, above all, he is pledged by the most
solemn ties to support the cause of right
and to foresee the occasions of wrong which
a less highly trained man might not detect.

He is a kind of over-father, bound to support the parental authority of his elder sons,
and the filial rights of his younger children,
to balance, to decide, to warn, to encourage,
to dissuade along those lines which he believes will be most conducive to the highest
good of his clients in particular and of

the whole community in general; and the highest proof of these assertions is to be found in the fact that his flock after all willingly yield to him the rights to which his position entitles him: mothers consult him about their sons, fathers about their wives, children about their home duties. It is a pleasant sight, I say, to see Father Thorpe go along the street; a butcher-boy grins in his face, calls him father, and lifts, not touches, his cap; he claps Jim upon the cheek, and Mary on the head; he bids Selina take out that unbecoming feather; frowns indulgently upon Tom at the corner by the public-house; and tells his dear child Mrs. Johnson "not to talk nonsense": and all that the Protestant world can do is to cry "priestcraft" and "Popery," and thank God that her ministers know their place better than that.

Lastly, how strange it is that this state of affairs should be brought about through the seminary training!

It has always been supposed, and indeed

publicly stated by dignitary after dignitary
of the Establishment, that what Englishmen
wanted was a pastorate that consisted of
religious men of the world who could meet
their flocks upon equal terms; University
men, gentlemen, public-school men — no
others need apply. The seminary system
continues to be denounced at every meeting
convened for the discussion of clerical education; it is supposed that isolation, enforced
prayer, precise regulation of time, separa-
tion from female society, even celibacy itself
tends to produce an unreal temper of mind,
a race of clergymen with their heads on
one side and an unnatural speaking-voice,
a ministry which may indeed perform sacerdotal duties with a correct deportment,
but which is utterly incompetent to deal
with men on equal terms, or to descend
to the dusty arena of domestic and civil
life.

Yet precisely the opposite appears to be
the case. If I wish to smoke my pipe with
a congenial clergyman, or to hear reasonable conversation on topics of the day, or to

learn how to deal with a refractory child, or
to discuss the advisability of attending a
certain race-meeting; or if, on the other
hand, I need a little brisk consolation, or
have an unpleasant secret to reveal, or an
inveterate habit to overcome, or a complicated moral problem to unravel, I should
not dream of stepping across to the rectory
or to the new vicarage of St. Symphorosa.
In the former I should find a loud-voiced,
thumping sort of a man, educated after a
fashion at the University, and certainly a
warm-hearted, generous soul, but also unable to understand my point of view or do
anything but proclaim his own; in the latter
an anæmic starveling — anæmic, it is true,
by nature, and starveling by the grace of
a mortified life — praiseworthy defects —
who would do his utmost to raise my
thoughts to higher things, and to induce me
to come to his new oaken-lined vestry next
Saturday and open my grief in his pale ear.
On the other hand, I should unhesitatingly
take my hat and go across to the Popish
presbytery, where I should find a man who

had spent ten years of his youth in a rigid
seminary, but who had somehow emerged
from it a man of the world in the best sense,
neither a large-hearted bully nor a spiritual
hypochondriac; one who will neither shout
at me nor shrink from me, who will possibly
drop his aspirates and be entirely ignorant
of literature and art, but who will yet listen
to what I have to say, understand me when
I say it, and give me excellent advice. I
am confident that he will hold his tongue,
for he has no Eve to tempt him to indiscre-
tion; he will wear no frown of absorption,
for he has a thousand secrets more weighty
than my own; he will not attempt to
proselytize my soul, for, as he justly says,
if the Catholic Church is right, it is I
that will have to go to Hell, not he; —
who will, in short, although he is two
years my junior, be to me exactly what
my father was twenty years ago; tell me
frankly that I have been a fool, advise
me how to repair my folly, and then be
equally willing to talk about something
else.

Yes, yes; the Catholic Church is amazingly adroit; she has managed to produce grapes from thorns, and figs from thistles, and men of the world from seminaries. I have not an idea how she does it, unless her own explanation of it is true — which is that the knowledge of God is the short cut to knowledge of man, that time spent in prayer is the most economical investment of a working hour, and that meditation on supernatural mysteries and familiarity with supernatural things confer an insight into ordinary affairs of common life that can be obtained in no other way: unless once more Christ's own words are to be taken literally, not metaphorically, and that when He said that those who for His sake renounced wives and children and brethren and lands, should find themselves treated as husbands and fathers and brothers in their turn, that they who lost their life should find it, that they who took the lowest place should presently stand in the highest, and that the meek and the peacemakers should inherit the earth, be called the children of God, shine out as the light of the world, and be set up upon a high hill, a city that cannot be hid.

Yes; there is no doubt about it at all. If ever I find myself in serious trouble I shall go to a Catholic priest to extricate me from it. . . .

THE SENSE OF THE SUPERNATURAL

MARCH, 1904.

My cousin George is beginning to obsess me, as the mediæval theologians say. He has paid me another visit, and the aroma of his personality still lingers about my room.

I have allowed him to see portions of my previous remarks upon him; and since he is entirely good-humoured, he professed himself flattered rather than annoyed. "My dear fellow," he said, "it is very good of you to be so much interested. It's quite true; I have never had any religious sense that I can remember. It seems to me that I get on all right without it; and as for dreariness — well, it seems to me that a fool's paradise is considerably more dreary than the pleasant little town in which you

have placed me.   That at any rate exists;
even you allow that.   The other does not,
at least I do not allow that it does, and you
cannot prove it. . . . For God's sake, let's
talk about something else!"

Now, what is to be made of this phenomenon? Is one bound to confess then, after
all, that the religious sense is like a taste for
music or a fancy for travel; and that men
may fulfil the purpose of their existence
equally well, lacking it? . . .

Let me expand the thesis, and in doing
so, reassure myself.

A sense of music or a taste for travel are
facts to be accounted for: it is perfectly
true that many persons appear to exist in
comfort without them; but it is another
question as to how far the world without
them could exist at all.

America, for example, would still be
represented on our maps by leagues of
barren water if Columbus had not been
inspired with a divine frenzy.   St. James's
Hall would never have raised its head in
Piccadilly, nor the opera-house stood in

Bayreuth, if Beethoven and Wagner had not been moved by an impulse, that not even they themselves could explain, to scribble dots and dashes on and between five lines arranged like a hurdle. The world would have been a poorer place without these inexplicable emotions which hard-headed persons may denounce as secretions of the liver, but which yet have crossed seas, climbed mountains, discovered inspiration in the crash of brass, melted lovers' hearts by a contact of a horse's mane and the clockwork of a cat, wakened the dead to life, and set the world a-singing.

Or consider again those qualities which all men approve and by which all profit, and yet which none can justify. Such things as chivalry, or the conquest of the strong by the weak; self-sacrifice, which only becomes sublime when the certain is immolated for the sake of the uncertain, or the greater for the less, or the known for the unknown, as when a mature mother rejoices to die for an impossible child — these things can be defended by no argu-

ments which George is capable of adducing.
On the contrary, they can be mercilessly
condemned by the code to which he is so
fond of appealing. The Survival-of-the-
Fittest, the Struggle-for-Existence, stride
down on them like giant slayers; but I
have yet to meet the materialist who, when
the crisis was imminent, would not inter-
vene in this massacre of the innocents.

Religious Emotion, then, is content to
take her stand by these illogical sisters of
hers, and wait radiantly for the world's
acquittal. "See what I have done for you,"
she cries with confident eyes and glowing
cheeks. "Have I not, also, crossed seas,
rescued captives, climbed high hills, haled
you to Paradise, hung with you over the
red mouth of hell, called you hither and
thither, and shown you things to come?
Have I not saved you from crime when
reason urged you on, lighted the lamps
when sense had put them out, strengthened
weak knees, and made the lame to leap;
opened blind eyes and deaf ears, painted
the dull world with glory? And if these

are too flimsy proofs by which to justify
myself, — have I not laboured in quarries,
and retranslated them into arch and pinnacle
and fretted spire? Have I not walled off
sweet houses of peace when all men were
at war? Have I not tuned your fiddles,
blown your organs, sung through human
throats, set dead words alight, and lifted
you in spite of yourself and death and hell
and adverse circumstance? Have I not
walked with you as children, held your
hands in dangerous paths, comforted you
with better gifts than health or wealth,
whispered secrets to you when you lay
dying? Then, can you not be content to
suffer me to exist, even if you do not know
my birth or origin? Is it not enough that
I came to you through the door of your
heart, and that my friends are Art and
Chivalry — such friends that we live and
die together, for if you slay me you will find
them dead by my side."

This then seems to be her answer to
the jeer that religion cannnot be proved.
Certainly it cannot, at least in the sense

of an exact science; but neither can nine
tenths of what we take for granted.   I
cannot prove the beauty of a Gloire-de-
Dijon, or the honesty of my friend, or the
pleasure of incipient drunkenness; yet I
do not for that reason disregard them as
merely subjective impressions, true for me
but doubtful for another.   On the contrary,
I walk into my garden to enjoy myself; I
lend John five pounds; I refrain from
more than two glasses of beer; — with
complete confidence that my motives are,
if not reasonable, at least emotional, and
not in the least to be less depended upon
for that account.

Or consider it from another point of
view.

The dulness of irreligious people is a
fact beyond question: they yawn in one
another's company.   I am perfectly prepared therefore to advance to meet them,
and declare that their philosophy is too
dull to be true.

Their answer is that the philosophy

which I represent is too good to be true;
the world would be too lively to hold together if miracles and conversions and such
things were any more than agreeable illu-
sions. And to that again I answer by an
analogy which they are bound to respect.

I tell them, out of their own mouth, that
phenomena of unassisted nature are only
uninteresting to those who are too blind to
see. A dust-heap, for example, or a stretch
of sand, or a slope of grass, is dull only to
the eyes of unperceptive persons. Dulness,
then, is not a fact but an illusion; it lies
in the brain, not in the object perceived.
There is simply no limit to the range of
interest which lies at the feet of every man.
The telescope or the microscope do no more
than take him a step further along the road
of the infinite. Fact is not only stranger
than fiction, it is far larger as well. They
must allow me, then, to apply that canon to
matters perceived by the religious sense.
These are ranges of thought, they tell me,
that are not worth a sensible man's ex-
amination. I answer that first, in their

own words, the "proper study of mankind
is man"; and therefore that to dismiss so
enormous a weight of what claims to be
actual experience, as inconsiderable, is to
confess to limitation and sectarianism:
secondly, that since, as again they confess,
truth is both larger and stranger than
fiction, it is beyond man's capacity to
imagine in excess of fact — he may picture
God as a family on Olympus, but he cannot attain to His infinity; he may believe
in witchcraft, but he cannot fathom the
abyss of spiritual malevolence that sur-
rounds him. The fact, then, that we can
imagine a Saviour indicates that there must
be one greater than our dreams; that we
picture the streets of the Heavenly City as
paved with gold, shows us that they are
paved with something much better; the
crowns of light to which we aspire must be
set with jewels, whose splendour we have
never seen, and be wrought in a workshop
of inconceivable glory. In other words,
"Eye hath not seen . . ." and the rest of
the quotation.

Yes, George, this is rank idealism expressed in frothy rhetoric. But remember that those two things have between them done more to make the world (which you find so excellent) what it is, than all you and your friends, and steamships, and Stock Exchanges, and Societies for the Propagation of Sound Thinking, would have done in twice the time. You yourself, for example, would not have existed if your father had not thought your mother to be what she was not, and grossly exaggerated what they both knew to be the truth; and no steamship would have been permitted to make foul our rivers and glad the hearts of our merchants, if Stephenson, or somebody else, had not dreamed that perhaps there was more in the kettle than water.

It would seem, then, that while individuals manage to exist without a taste for art, travel, or religion; yet that, first, as a matter of fact, half their life, and that the only half worth living, is generated from the products of these things, as well as two thirds more of what is left in the realm of

the purely material.   Remove the instincts
of art, exploration, and religion from the
world, and you are confronted by a set of
pigs, dwelling, at the very best, in mud
houses, covered with hair, ignorant of what
lies at the other side of the nearest tree,
doing nothing whatever but eating, drinking,
breathing, and begetting children in their
own likeness for which — (and no wonder)
— they have little affection and no hope. . . .

What, then, is to be said for people like
my second cousin?

There is a great deal to be said against
them; they are barbaric instead of cultivated, stupid instead of clever; and —
which they would resent being told more
than anything else, — retrograde instead of
progressive. What few advantages they have
— not over the rest of the world, but over
their savage ancestors — have accrued to
them through the enveloping atmosphere of
their friends and a certain strain of heredity.
They have received treasures of experience
by their birth and circumstances; and
though they are squandering these as rapidly

as possible, yet there are a few dingy coins still in their dusty cupboards which are sufficient, for the present, to ensure them a right of entry into decent society and a claim on the necessaries of life. My cousin would have had neither clothes to wear nor words in which to express his few and sterile thoughts if his ancestors had not been artists enough to understand that drapery was more elegant than blue woad, and their Roman invaders, murderers, and civilizers had not been mad enough to think that a journey in a painted boat was more romantic than the perpetual eating of olives in a villa: and it is obvious that if George had presented himself at my front door, naked, howling, and with a flint-hatchet, I should have been compelled to tell my maid that I was gone out to see a man.

Even if he had gained admittance I should not have understood him; nor he me. Yet when he actually came we were both moderately intelligible by one another, because he has somehow pilfered the use and meaning of a religious vocabulary that he professes to

despise. When he spoke of "life being
very pleasant in this little place," he ex-
plicitly recognized, first, the difference
between life and death, and therefore im-
plicitly the existence of Heaven and Hell;
second, the presence in man of an apprecia-
tive faculty whose roots spring from his
immortal soul; third, the laws of space
which lead us by an almost direct route
to the relations between spirit and matter,
the immanence and transcendency of God,
and even to the central mystery of the
Christian revelation. He confessed, too, his
indebtedness to scholastic grammarians,
since he guided his speech more or less
according to their injunctions; he bore
witness, by the use of his fourth word,
to the Norman invasion, itself undertaken
under the Church's blessing and sanction;
in fact, he showed himself to be the sub-
missive heir of the Christian ages, instead
of, as he fondly imagines, their dispassionate
subverter.

Yet there is even more to be said for him
than these pleas which he would so fiercely

reject, if he knew that I was putting them forward on his behalf.

When I ask myself why he did not strangle me as I stooped to poke the fire, I am bound to answer that I do not believe that he was restrained solely by his fear of the police. I think George to be a tolerably moral man. This of course, too, he would repudiate: the word "unmoral" is for ever on his lips: yet he leads a life that would put to shame a Christian baron of the Middle Ages. I am aware that he preaches the gospel of the fatherly cynic as he sits over his fire sometimes, with an impressionable young man; but like many other preachers, he would not even dream of practising the code which he proclaims.

I am forced, therefore, to the conclusion that the religious spirit dominates not only his vocabulary, his methods of thought, and his behaviour, but even the mind that underlies them and makes them what they are. In other words, he is a profoundly religious man.

He confesses in his life the existence of a

code on which he can offer no remarks worth hearing; and he perpetually gives the lie to his dictum that sin lies not in action but excess.

He avails himself thankfully of the innumerable advantages which the faith, hope, and love of his friends and ancestors provide so kindly for his support, though he refuses to acknowledge their source. He lies, like a child at his mother's breast, drinking the sweetness that he does not understand and the strength which makes him what he is: he guides his life by principles too bright for his enfeebled eyes to look upon. I hold, then, that mystically and effectually he grasps God, though he denies, so far as his starved and poisoned consciousness is concerned, that there is any such Person. Yet, when all is said, what he thinks of God, however, is not an important consideration; but what God thinks of him — and I have tried to show reason for believing that this is not altogether unfavourably — this is what matters.

THE MYSTICAL SENSE

April, 1904.

I HAVE been lately reading a book by
Mother Juliana of Norwich that a friend
has sent me; — I have been doing more
than read it, — it has been about my path,
and about my bed, so extraordinary is the
fascination of that holy woman. But I
do not want to say anything about her
particularly, because at present I have
nothing to say. I wish rather to clear
my own mind with regard to the general
issue.

Mysticism, as Mr. Marjoribanks told me,
with a somewhat sententious air, is "the
art of divine union." That seems to me
a fair definition, but like all short definitions, actually misleading, unless again one
defines it. We must begin further away
than that.

To-day I was looking out of my window, and saw what I suppose I have seen at least two hundred times before — an old chestnut tree outlined against the sky. I am slightly unwell; and, in spite of the obvious retort of the materialist, I must state my belief that at such times one occasionally sees beneath the surface of things in a very curious way. At any rate, I experienced a train of thought that ran somewhat as follows: —

There is that tree, I said to myself, entirely different from any other tree in the world. Some power or other prepared its seed, caused this weather and that to develop its possibilities, sent this wind and the other to bend it, this sunshiny day, that storm of rain, mellow days, biting nights, and so forth, for about seventy years. The same power brought it about that this morning was still and breathless, that the sky was pale blue, that I lifted my eyes from my book and noticed the drooping tracery, the aspiring twigs, that I continued to notice it instead of returning to my book. Now, what does that all mean?

If we postulate two things about the Power, namely, that it is Personal and Infinite, the meaning of that series of links is simply inevitable. It was brought about that I might see it all, — I — *moi qui vous parle* — among other reasons, — that I might discern one tiny detail of the immense character that is in some fashion legible beneath the outward appearance of what I choose to call Creation.

Now, is not this one illustration of one department of what men have agreed to call mysticism? I do not mean that I possess that faculty — in fact, my failure to understand the meaning of the tree is a sign, I suppose, that I do not; but if a trained mystic had been sitting in my chair I cannot doubt that he would have learned something, or, more probably, perceived one more example of some principle he had already grasped. He would have looked through the tree, or still better, perhaps, into it, and seen some divine thing.

Almighty God, I take it, has made the world, and arranged causes and their effects, with at least this purpose among others — that the more intelligent of His creatures may apprehend a little more of His character than is possible to them in any other way. A kind of silence seems to fall upon the soul as one considers this. . . .

Once upon a time three men stood side by side looking at a field — a farmer, a geologist, and a poet. The farmer saw the quality of the soil, the geologist the tilt of the strata, the poet the curves and colours. Each in the evening, for his own reasons, wrote a report of what he had seen. The farmer used a number of technical terms, recommending his friend to buy the five-acre; the geologist added a foot note in his book illustrative of some important theory; the poet composed a sonnet and published it in the *Westminster Gazette*. Each, in plain language, had seen the same thing, and yet each, in equally plain language, had seen a totally different thing.

A kind of silence, I say, envelops me when I think of this. I do not any longer want to laugh at materialists, or sneer at scientists; they appear to me in a light of indescribable pathos: they are perfectly right in what they say — at any rate I cannot, and do not even wish, to prove them wrong; but what is so sad about them is that, while they may be perfectly right within their own limits, they think that those limits are coincident with the range of human knowledge. There they go, with their carpet bags, and specimens, spectacled and profound, philosophically enthusiastic, thinking that it all matters very much; and there stares at the brisk group, maybe, from a wayside cottage some dirty child, finger in mouth, who knows more than them all. It is true that he does not know whether he lives on chalk or gravel, or of what chemicals his own body is composed; yet he has looked wide-eyed at a running stream, and paused, stone in hand, to hear one more phrase from the plump thrush, and a world has opened —

ah! why be rhetorical in a matter of such
bewildering simplicity? . . .

This, then, seems to me to be one of the
more elementary functions of the mystical
sense — to look through the outward and to
— I do not say understand, but — apprehend some glimmer of the Character that
lies beyond.   What is so seen is usually
incapable of statement, though that astonishing woman, Mother Juliana of Norwich,
attempts it sometimes.

He showed me a little thing [she writes], the
quantity of a hazel-nut, in the palm of my hand;
and it was as round as a ball.   I looked thereupon
with the eye of my understanding, and thought,
What may this be?   And it was answered generally
thus: *It is all that is made.* . . .   In this little
thing I saw three properties.   The first is that God
made it; the second is that God loveth it; the
third that God keepeth it.   But what is to me
verily the Maker, the Keeper and the Lover — I
cannot tell; for till I am substantially united with
Him, I may never have full rest nor true bliss.

What a stammering explanation; and
yet is it not evident what the good woman

is after? Neither you nor I can say what it is, and yet we both know.

I wonder what she would have had to say of my chestnut tree this morning.

Now, it appears to me that this slow stare upon nature is enough work for any man all his life long; for consider the amazing contradictions that he sees; there is love, patience, beauty; and there is also hatred, impatience, and ugliness, all equally obvious and eloquent. What kind of a Character then must be deduced? I do not know in the least; I think the fault lies in our attempt to deduce such anthropomorphic fancies at all; we must be content to take the symbols as they stand. And yet I, and I suppose everybody else, have had moments when the mystery seemed on the point of disclosure, when, in one sense, it was disclosed. We cannot remember it afterwards, still less can we express it even to ourselves; we cannot do better than say with Mother Juliana, *I saw God in a point.*

Yet this slow stare is only the outset of

the mystical life; there follows what is even
greater, the using of what is seen as a
means of union with the Divine Character;
and here I must confess even my pre-
sumptuous pen falters. If I have taken
two hours over what I have written, it
would take me the rest of my life to set
down what remains within even my narrow
horizons.   I touch only with the tips of my
fingers the mystery of what they call the
Way of Union; I can only picture it under
a variety of images so grotesque that I dare
not face their discussion. Embracing a
globe, drinking from a cup, plunging into
a sea, the effort of relaxing effort, consum-
mating a marriage — all these odd phrases
have been employed by saints, and it is best
to leave it at that. I can only discern
figures moving on mountains against the
sky, to whom, I know, these phrases are
not nonsense, figures whom I envy more
than I can describe, to whom a sense has
been given which transcends that of the
artist as the artist's that of the mathema-
tician, who have looked so long that at last

they have begun to move in curious spasmodic efforts as ludicrous as those of a marionette, who stand at such an angle that they see lights and curves invisible to other men (as one may bend his head to catch the purple of a shot silk), and who have in some fashion made the colour their own.

I had better stop, and go and look at my tree again. After all, the mystical sense is not an essential, though its cultivation may be a duty. God has not left us to depend upon what we can find out for ourselves, if what Catholics say is true. He has given us, it seems (because I suppose we were so stupid and wilful), a more plainly written book, in which we may read His Character; and He has lived Himself the life that He would have us live. That is enough for simple folk like me: I cannot improve upon the Gospel. And yet sometimes I cannot help envying those who can verify what they have been told; to whom Calvary is not an incident, but a continuous state, as

plain to their eyes as the colour of a chestnut tree; who can look upon lilies and consider them to some purpose; who stand
always in a hush of silence more articulate
than the sound of words. . . .

HOLY WEEK

April, 1904.

It is Easter morning as I write this in my garden, and attempt to sum up my impressions of last week. Yet I know even as I begin that it is useless. What I can write down bears about as much relation to what I experienced as a child's scratching on a slate to, let us say, the sunrise burning over the sea. However, I cannot rest till I have made my scratches, and tried to embody in words what even my soul itself could only dimly apprehend. Even as I put down these words I am aware that the light is coarsening. And it is really a serious reflection that even all that my stupid dulness could perceive is only as a shadow of a shadow of what the Church was trying to show me.

Tenebrae

Well, I have been witnessing a four days'
drama of the most appalling kind.   To be
plain with myself, it has been nothing else
than the tragedy of the murder of God; and
that interwrought with the most bewildering
pangs and motives, and overshot with gleams
of love and pity.   All kinds of personages
have been moving on the stage, clever,
shallow souls, lovers, foes, simple, passionate, stupid, fiery-eyed, self-seeking, imper-
ceptive — why pile up epithets ? — in short,
the entire human race.   And in the midst
God has been walking, dumb, with gestures,
lifting His Hands in useless explanation, in
appeal, in agony, dropping them in despair.
And beneath the stage, like a Greek chorus,
have crowded the saints and sages of all
time, chanting comment and interpretation,
running now on to the higher platform, now
abased in the dust twisting like worms, now
turning to cry to me, gesticulating what I
was too dull to understand.   Or it has been
a shadow-show, with liturgy for the sheet,
and the Person of God for the light: great

confused movements have come and gone;
and, from behind, groaning and singing,
death-screams and laughter, have continually sounded. And at the end the great
Mother of us all has turned to me, smiling
and weeping. "Well," she has said to me,
"you have seen the shadow of the shadow
of truth — a little coarse daub of reality.
What have you to say? . . . Have you anything to say? . . . What do you think of
yourself and God now?"

Where, then, can I begin? I suppose
with Tenebrae.

Each evening, for three nights, we as-
sembled towards dusk, taking our seats in
the echoing stone church, and waited, looking up at the cold altar and the stone-floored
sanctuary. There were a few lights here
and there, enough to read by, and on the
right stood a peak of burning candles.
There came a sound of footsteps, and
through the gloom came two priests walking slowly, followed by a troop of men and
boys; presently they were in their places,

and after a silence, simple as a country
show began the play.

Now, I do not propose to talk liturgi-
cally, but merely to describe my general
impressions.

It seemed to me that each evening,
deepening in power and pathos each time,
a kind of gigantic Figure grew upon the
dark air. I scarcely know who He was:
sometimes it was simply He whom we call
Jesus Christ. Yes, I think it was He,
really, all the while; but it was not as I had
always pictured Him to myself, and as the
plain Gospel presents Him. It was much
more than that. I saw emotions, agonies,
and smiles, that I had not suspected.
Strange persons, curious old prophets, veiled
shadows, seemed to hold up lanterns to
light Him, and to voice what He left unsaid.
Evening by evening He stood there, moved
from side to side, groaned, yearned, ex-
postulated, explained, and suffered; "Save
me, O God!" He moaned; "the waters
are come in even to my soul. . . . I am

become a stranger to my brethren . . .
God, help me! Lord, delay not! . . . Leave
me not! . . ." And when words failed Him,
His comforters who could not help Him,
took up His lamentation; telling us that
His travail was the travail of the world,
and pointing us to the City of God itself,
lying desolate through His woe. Yes, it
was Jesus Christ; but I have never before
understood what it was that He meant
when He named Himself *Son of Man.*

For it was all mankind that stood there
in His Person — He Himself became sin
and ruin Incarnate, He was Penitent as well
as Priest, Sinner as well as Saviour, a worm
and no man, as well as Eternal God. For an
hour or two each evening I saw heaven and
earth as one thing — glory and shame
rushed together into one whirling core of
agony: despair and hope, faith and darkness, love and hate, fused before my eyes.
The infinite expressed itself finitely, and the
finite soared into the illimitable — and the
pity of all was that the supreme horror was
enacted in a Heart like my own. *The*

Word became Flesh. The infinite sea was compressed into the compass of a single soul.

Well, well; it is of no use to write like this! But does no one understand, any more? . . .

What deepened the terror was the extinction of the candles. One by one the stars went out, with frightful deliberation, and each was like the putting out of an eye, or the slow turn of a rack. My heart cried out for a blaze of light, protesting against dying in the dark; but one by one, with long pauses they went out. (Did that man in the surplice, I wonder, know what he was doing?) There was only one left after a while; but of that I shall speak presently.

Now at times there was a break in that monotonous recital of pain. One at a lectern chanted out a comment in a kind of wailing melody that rose and fell, as a dying man who has been long silent might croon out a tune, very slowly, note by note, up and down; and, then, as if the tension

would break our hearts altogether, there
came a gush of lamentable harmony, that
was like the sudden smell of autumn and
the ruddy gleam of sunset, penetrating a
silent death-chamber.

"O Jerusalem! Jerusalem!" sang the
boys, "turn to the Lord thy God." That
was all.

Well, well; even at this distance of time,
writing as I am in the sunlit glory of Easter
morning, it seems as if I could not bear it.
But worse was to come.

We were stilled at last, all of us, I think
into a kind of resignation. It seemed useless to strive. We were driven down into
the lowest depth, and lay there passive and
helpless, as Jesus turned His great eyes
upon us out of His drawn, sunken Face, lit
only by a single flame. There was no more
to be said. He was there, and we could not
help Him. God said it was to be so. And
then the cruelty waxed tenfold more poig-
nant; for, no sooner had we come to this,
and yielded to the darkness and misery,

than far above us, out of sunlight, our great
Mother lifted up her voice and sang like
the Cherubim —

"Blessed be the Lord God of Israel,
for He hath visited and redeemed His
people."

I think I could have borne anything but
that. If I had but been left alone, there
was nothing that I could not suffer now;
but that happy song was as a sword for
pain. Is it anything for wonder that even
as I write these words, my eyes are blinded
again with tears? Oh, the cruelty of let-
ting the light into that pit! Yet she did
so, flooding us with sorrow upon sorrow,
and shame upon shame; and Jesus Himself sobbed, there, before my eyes, with
the exquisite torment. Oh! could she not
leave us with the tears of Jeremias, and the
soft moaning of David — but that she must
mock and pierce us with joy? Yet she
sang on and on . . .

"And thou, child, shalt be called the
Prophet of the Highest. . . . To give knowledge of salvation unto His people. . . .

Through the tender mercy of our God,
whereby the dayspring from on high hath
visited us: To give light to them that sit
in darkness and the shadow of death; to
guide our feet into the way of peace."

There was a sudden silence; and a voice
cried savagely —

"But the traitor gave them a sign, saying: 'Whom I shall kiss is He, hold Him.'"

And the second night —

"They placed above His Head His cause
written, Jesus of Nazareth, King of the
Jews."

And the third night —

"Women sitting at the selpulchre la-
mented, weeping for the Lord."

Ah! we were back again at the bottom
of the pit, plunged deep, and hope had died
again, and Heaven was closed, and Jesus
stared at us, streaked with blood, expres-
sionless, blank, and white-faced, rigid and
all but dead; and one wailing voice began —

"Christ was made obedient for us unto
death, . . ." and again silence.

Then a quick, hurried muttering began, as of men in desperate fear at the brink of death, hastily, hopelessly, as if repeating some charm in despair, on one low, babbling note.

"Have mercy upon me, O God, after thy great goodness," and so through the psalm.   Then I saw what I had not noticed, and that was that the church was completely dark.   There was not a glimmer left.   I could see the pale line of surplices on either side of the wide choir, a great pillar grey against the dusk and rising into complete darkness; the solemn pallor of the vaulting.   Then, as a voice began from the dark figure kneeling on the bare steps, a flicker shone for an instant in the apse, and a monstrous shadow moved across it. Again silence and complete darkness, then a crash that shook my heart and tore a gasp from my lips, echoing round and round like the roar of doom; and in the stillness that followed a man came out from behind the altar, carrying a single candle. That was the end — darkness, and one star.

II

Of the Maundy Mass, the Sepulchre, and the bloodless sacrifice of Good Friday, it is even harder to write; for instead of one profound emotion there are a thousand; and I could not follow them. It was as a hand dashed across a jubilant harp, and of the incoherent murmur there may be a hundred meanings. Is it in the sombre bass, or the mellow mid notes, or the ecstatic trebles that the secret lies?

First, then, the Maundy Mass. The altar is ablaze with lights and gold and flowers, and from a side chapel comes the glow of the expectant tomb. Three priests are there, gorgeous and brilliant; the Mass begins as usual, quietly splendid; and, at the intonation of the *Gloria* there is an event, to me, at any rate, unexpected, which floods the whole soul with a passion that may rise from either torment or bliss. For, as the priest's voice ends, there is a crashing chord from the great organ, and a tumult of bells; and as if a whole heaven of sound had split, the mad riot pours on, moment after moment. The chords melt, change, wax in volume; the air is full of the throbbing bass of the bourdon, the windy bellowing of the tower, and the shrill silver tinkle of the tiny bells gathered from every altar in the church, to greet the new-born Eucharist — on and on till the heart is torn and vibrating, and the brain exalted with music: the three priests sign themselves with the Cross, and there is silence.

When the Mass is over, sung throughout unaccompanied, with a kind of quiet joy the procession is formed, and the Body of the Lord is borne, wafted along on *Pange Lingua*, to the waiting sepulchre, where It shall lie for a day and a night. The walls are decked with flowers, and sheaves of candles stand on either side. There it is laid in solemn joy, censed, and left.

Yet the whole affair is not what it seems. It has an air of sorrow beneath the beauty, that rises like the indefinable scent of death from a coffin piled high with flowers and walled with lights. Oh, yes! the vestments are white and gold, the organ peals, the candles flame; but it is no good. It is desperately hard to keep up the exultation. The mind assents, as always, to the liturgical instinct that rejoices over the inauguration of the marriage-supper of the Lamb, but the heart remembers that the Meat and Wine upon the board have been made possible only by the death of the Lamb whom we love. "Eat and drink," cries Wisdom, "see the wine that I have mingled and the bread that I break to you. Lift up your hearts and sing." But as we watch her, her eyes are full of secret pain, and on her lips a grievous paleness.

It is indeed like that First Supper of which the Gospel tells. "Now is the Son of Man glorified," cries Jesus, with shining eyes and broken Heart, "and God is glorified in Him. . . ." "And when they had sung an hymn they went forth to the mount of Olives." Singing and praising

they went out, desperately feigning that
all was well; they looked upon the Golden
Vine in the Temple courts in the glory of
the paschal moon. . . . And there followed
the Agony and the Sweat of Blood.

I looked into the church again that afternoon towards sunset, and I knew that I was
right. There was the *chapelle ardente* before me, one avenue of white flowers and
yellow flames, heavy and redolent, and in
the midst, enthroned, lay Jesus Christ in
state; not as when He beams through the
tabernacle door instinct with life, but with
an aspect of dreadful death. His guards
were two children, come in from the school
next door, with white veils on their heads;
and, as I knelt and looked, they presently
stood and stretched out their arms cross-
wise, to remember Him better. So they
stood, minute after minute, till the slender
arms drooped and trembled and rose again
resolutely, striving to explain in gesture
their pity and love. "Come, then, at Thy
Will, heavenly Physician," cried Richard
the hermit six centuries ago, "kindle in my

heart a spark of Thy passion, of love and of pity, to quicken it with."

Yet Jesus was not dead yet. But to this Church who lives in eternity, who still greets Mary as she kneels in Nazareth, and views the Judge coming even now upon the clouds of heaven — this Church to whom time is nothing, to whom space is nothing — nothing more than imagined lines on the globe of eternity — since she adores the Body of God at one moment in ten thousand places — to this Church all things are possible. She buries her Lord on Thursday and raises Him on Friday, crucifies Him ten minutes later, and sings her Easter Mass while He yet lies in the tomb. It is all one to her — Calvary, Bethlehem, Heaven — for she "*sees God in a point.*"

On Friday, then, the climax comes, and it is as simple as the death of a child.

First, then, I saw three priests in black and white approach the altar. There was some reading from a book, a collect or two, the singing of the Passion — a long song of mournful recitative by various voices; a number of prayers. The peace and stability of the Church, a blessing on Christ's Vicar, the Bishop of the diocese, on all clerks, catechumens, and the world, comfort for mourners, conversion for heretics, Jews, and heathens — this was what was asked as we stood on Golgotha. Then followed the adoration of the Cross.

How can I describe that, except by saying that it was the simplest thing I have ever seen, as clear and natural as a pool of water, and yet as bitter as brine? The crucifix, laid as if for tenderness' sake on a soft cushion, is approached by all who are present. I, too, went up — I, a heretic and outcast, for Jesus Christ came to save sinners — and I knelt there, trembling, between two boys who seemed to tend that wounded Figure, wiping His feet softly after each kiss. And I kissed the smooth ivory, too, above the nail . . . and He did not strike me!

One thing, too, I saw: an old woman came up the stones on her knees, moaning

and muttering, wrapped in a shawl; and
she kissed Him, as a mother might, on His
pierced feet, His bruised knees, His wounded
side. . . . My God! how beautiful that was!
And all the while there pealed the reproaches.

"Oh! My people, what have I done to
thee? In what have I grieved thee? Tell
me! Tell me! I brought thee out of
Egypt: and thou hast prepared a cross
for thy Saviour."

Then followed a roar of Greek, strange
and sonorous:

*Agios O Theos . . . Agios ischyros . . . Agios athanatos
eleeson imas.*

So, as in a delirium a man talks in a long-
forgotten tongue, now, when her heart is
rent, the Catholic Church drops twenty
centuries without an effort, and speaks as
she spoke underground in Rome, and in
Paul's hired house, and in Crete and Alex-
andria and Jerusalem.

"I planted thee, My lovely vineyard,"
moaned the choir, "and thou hast been
bitter to Me. With vinegar thou didst
quench My thirst, and with a lance didst

pierce the Side of thy Saviour. . . . I
scourged Egypt for thee; and thou hast
given Me to scourging. . . . I drowned
Pharaoh for thy sake, and thou hast be-
trayed Me to the priests. . . . I opened a
way for thee through the Red Sea, and
with a lance thou hast opened My side. . . .
I fed thee with manna in the wilderness,
and thou hast wounded Me with blows
and scourgings. . . . I gave thee wholesome water from the rock, and thou hast
given Me gall and vinegar. . . . I gave
to thee a royal sceptre, and thou hast
crowned Me with thorns. . . . Oh! My
people, what have I done to thee, that thou
dost use Me so?"

Then we went all together to the tomb,
and brought out His very Body, shouting
as we went in terrible glee how the banners
of the King go forth, glorifying the Cross
that we made for Him and on which He
hangs, praising the Fount of Salvation.
We laid It upon the altar, censed It in
silence, and so moved on to the end, in
incoherent haste.

There is no sacrifice on this day, for all
is sacrifice. There is no need for the Holy
Ghost to come down, to make the Body of
the Son, and touch the Father's Heart, for
to-day all the world is Calvary. Yet frag-
ments of the Mass are uttered as by a
dreaming priest. The *Paternoster* is sung;
the prayers are said, the Host is consumed;
and, in an instant all is over; the black
clouds topple over, the gulf is filled, the
rending rocks are still again; and I — I was
as a man who awakes and sees the sunlight
in his room. . . .

HOLY SATURDAY

"As when a man awakes and sees the
sunlight in his room." This is the secret
of Holy Saturday.

Many years ago I was in Italy, where
the air is like water, and the water like
wine. Morning by morning I awoke to
the crying of the swifts outside, drawing
long icy breaths of freshness, seeing the
netted sunshine shake on the ceiling from

the jug of water on the floor, hearing the rustle of the leaves below my window. There, in Italy, the morning struck the key of the day; the world was alive there, and as good as God made it, and everything was in His hand. . . .

Now on Holy Saturday the Catholic Church is in just such a mood as that. She is as simple as the sunshine, as happy as the birds, as melodious as the rustle of branches. But it is morning, not noon. Christ is rising, but not yet in mid-heaven; and she springs from her bed of sorrows to make all ready for Him. He will be here presently.

First, then, there must be fire to meet Him with, lights and torches, for the garden is yet in tender twilight; and there must be water to wash Him with, to take clean away the smell of the tomb, and the aloes, and the myrrh. He being dead, dieth no more. Water too, not vinegar, for Him to drink — light again and water through which He may be seen and handled by her blinder children — for is He not the Light

of the World and the Water of Life? —
light and water once more, that He may
lighten those that sit in darkness and satisfy
those that thirst after righteousness.

So we went down in the early dawn, all
together, the priests still in purple, leading
us to where a brazier burned in the porch.
From outside blew in the morning breeze,
carts rattled over the stones, contemptuous
strangers eyed us through the door. But
it did not matter; we were bent on great
affairs.

First the red coals were blessed, for is
not the Church the Lady-Mistress of the
world? — all things are hers, for she is
Christ's and Christ is God's. Those coals
had been lighted from a flint, for God's
Spouse is older than the Stone Age, as well
as younger than yesterday, God is named
by her as the Father of Lights — an exquisite title — and begged to bless this fire
because He made it and loves it. It is
Brother Fire now, as that dear child St.
Francis called it. He must not rage and
storm any more; he must burn demurely

in lamps, and if he dances it must only be
piously and on the summit of a candlestick.
Then five large gilded things are blessed
and sprinkled with the last drops of holy
water.   I whispered to a boy to tell me what
they were — for we were all very homely
and happy in the porch that morning — and
he told me, Incense for the Candle.

Then the deacon took off his purple, and
put on instead a large white dalmatic, stiff
with gold.   He took into his hand a pole
surmounted by three twisted candles and
wreathed with flowers, and went through
into the church.   When I came after, just
behind the others, he was lighting it from
the new holy fire.   Then he straightened it,
and there was a flame like a yellow flower
perched on one of the wicks; he knelt, and
simultaneously sang out at the top of his
voice —

Lumen Christi!

And the choir roared —

"Thanks be to God!"

Three times he did that, raising his voice
a tone or two at each repetition.   He did

not sing it very well: but did that matter?
For we were going even now with Mary
and Salome through the scented garden;
virgins to meet the Bridegroom, lovers to
keep tryst with the Beloved; and the three
lights swayed as we went.

There was a little going to and fro at the
altar, as we of the laity — and I, not even
of that — stumbled into our seats; and
when I had regained my composure, that
deacon was standing at a lectern, drawing
a long breath, with a little group about him
attentive and eager. Beyond, not a yard
away, stood the huge bronze candlestick.

Then he began to sing. . . .

It was a song such as none but a Christian could ever sing. It soared, dropped,
quavered, leapt again, laughed, danced,
rippled, sank, leapt once more, on and on,
untiring and undismayed, like a stream
running clear to the sea. Angels, earth,
trumpets, Mother Church, all nations and
all peoples sang in its singing. We, "dearest
brothers," as he named us (and I a heretic!),
were bidden to join with him — *him*, he

said in charming parenthesis, who was quite unworthy of being numbered among the Levites, — in imploring God Almighty and Merciful, to glorify this wax-candle through Jesus Christ who lives and reigns through all ages. We were to lift up our hearts, to thank God, because such was fitting. It was He who had paid the debt of Adam, and washed us in His Blood. This is the day and this the night on which Israel came out of Egypt, and the pillar of fire burned through the dark. This is the night of supremest grace, for Christ rose in it, burst the bands of death, and soared from Hell. O inestimable love of charity! O most necessary sin of Adam! O blessed, blessed fault which brought down such a Redeemer! O more than blessed night! For this is the night that is clear as the day. This is the night that banishes darkness, washes sins, gives innocence to the foul, and joy to the unhappy — that puts hatred to flight, brings peace to the birth, and all things in subjection to Jesus Christ!

Have you ever heard such a song as this?
— such a wealth of divine contradiction,
delirious paradox, and childlike wisdom?

Presently, after fixing the five incense
grains into the soft wholesome wax-candle
— (it was at least twelve feet high, by-the-
way) — he was off again in his song, be-
seeching God this time to receive this
evening sacrifice, prepared from the labour of
bees by the pains of Holy Church. Then
he lit the candle, and it was lifted to its
place high above all heads, while he drew a
lesson or two from its composition. Then
as boys dispersed in all directions, each
with a taper tipped with holy fire, to light
every lamp in the place, the deacon settled
down again indefatigably in his praises of
this holy night, and in his entreaties that
God would hear his singing, and see the
burning candle and bless every one in the
world, clergymen, people, and Pope. And
so he ended; and I, in my stiff pew, smiled
all over my face with sheer joy and love.

I thought a great deal about it all as I
sat down for the next three quarters of

an hour while the interminable prophecies
were read. I had meant to attend to them,
but I was far too much moved. Of course
I had read about these ceremonies, but I
had never seen them before, nor heard that
amazing song. . . . I wonder if any one
will think me irreverent in my thoughts.
They will be wrong if they do, for I am
as sure as I can be, that this is more or less
what the Catholic Church meant me to
think. She wished me to be as happy as
a child — happy because Jesus Christ was
risen; and because she was happy. . . .
Well, well; I must get on.

The blessing of the water was as joyous
as the blessing of the fire.

We all went down to the font, singing
that, as the hunted hart pants after water-
brooks, so panted our souls after God. We
were thirsty for God, we said, for tears had
been our only drink. Then we came to the
baptistery, and there was that deep, cool,
dusky pool of water shot through with one
clear sunbeam.

Here again God was prayed to bless the

sweetest of His elements — the water that washes souls — the water on which His Spirit moved — and to open a river of salvation to all that He has made. All evil things were to leave this cool, innocent creature; they were not to interfere with God Almighty's plans. And then, as if His Spirit indeed had given it life, the priest turned to that quiet pool and spoke to it as to a man.

"Yes: it is thee I bless, thou creature of water, thee whom God once set apart from dull earth; thee, who dost flow to us straight from Paradise in four streams; thee, who quenched Israel's thirst in Arabia. Yes; I bless thee, thou dear water, once turned into wine by Jesus Christ. He walked on thee with His blessed feet; He was baptized with thee by John; He poured thee from His Side; He sent thee out into all the world to wash His children's sins away.

"Then let God bless this creature, and send down His Holy Spirit — like — this — candle — into — it!"

There followed pourings of oil, — oil which, after all, is but water transmuted by divine power in the heart of the olive tree. And so presently we were back again, singing the Litany of the Saints with all our hearts, and the priests, for the last time, lay flat upon their faces like dead corpses before the altar. . . .

I cannot go on. Is it not too good to be true? And I have no part in it, anyhow. I was an intruder upon these secrets — for I am a heretic.

Or was I not rather like some child peering through the bars of a palace-garden? Within, royalty goes to and fro, music sounds, banners wave, bewildering glory moves up and down. But how happy it made me! And at least I have this encouragement, that though I may not yet receive the children's Bread — yet fire and water are the common heritage of all. God who has made the sun and the sea, who shines and rains upon just and unjust alike, will not be angry with me because I loved to see how He can deal with plain things, how He can make water holy as well as beautiful, and fire to lighten souls as well as eyes. . . .

Ah! there comes the crash of bells once more, the roar of the organ, as the white priests bow before the flaming altar: and there is no tragic silence to follow as on Thursday. All is splendour now. . . .

Fire is holy . . . Water is clean. . . .

Christ is risen. . . .

God bless us all!

ON THE DANCE AS A RELIGIOUS EXERCISE

JUNE, 1904.

IT is a curious fact that while the impending catastrophe in Russia excites wide interest, the deposition of at least one of the arts from her throne is wholly unrecognized by the majority of those who form what are called the civilized nations of the world. Originally both dancing and acting had their representatives upon Olympus; now Melpomene and her sisters have come to dwell in scarcely even a genteel retirement in such places as Leicester Square and Drury Lane; but Olympus knows them no more.

This, possibly, is an overstatement of fact, but it is an understatement of theory; for in more than one pulpit with which I am acquainted the Muse of Make-Believe presents a punctual appearance on Sunday

evenings; yet in theory she is supposed to
be somebody else; she rants *incognita* in
surplice and coloured stole.   Dancing, too,
with an exception which I shall state presently, not only is deposed from her religious
throne — for an Englishman cannot be expected to count such benighted places as
Seville on Corpus Christi — but the children
of those who once venerated her now are
astounded at the profane follies of their
fathers, and consider that God Almighty
cannot but be insulted by the pious pran-
cings of the Hottentot.

I said, with one exception; and it is that
of which I wish to treat, for it is that which
has suggested to me the subject of this
paper.

I confess that I am not one of those
persons who think that it is an evidence of
their own spiritual superiority to misbehave
during the worship of other people.   The
Baedeker gentlemen and ladies — for I am
sure that is what they wish to be called —
who stare and talk in the churches of Italy
and France, and audibly contrast the pos-

sibly ill-shaven priest at the altar with their
cultivated vicar at home, to the disadvan-
tage of the former — these people rouse in
me no spirit of emulation. Possibly, my
own eleven o'clock Morning Prayer, Litany,
Ante-Communion and Sermon, which I
occasionally attend in the country, may be
infinitely more pleasing to my Maker than
the curious series of actions which can be
witnessed in such Catholic churches; yet
for all that I am not certain that the latter
is nothing better than a piece of insolence,
and I conceive it to be more proper to stand
still than to walk about, to hold my tongue
than to engage in conversation.

It was during High Mass, then, not in
France but in England, that the thought
first came into my mind that perhaps here
was a survival of the ancient religious
dance — that stately, magnificent series of
slow movements which surely may express
devotion of the most solemn and reverent
kind, as well as can the colour of vest-
ment or sanctuary, or the sounds of
melody.

I am aware that some writers on ceremonial declare that movements and postures
are nothing more than such as arise from
the necessity of going from one place to
another, and of standing still; and that each
such movement and posture must find its
justification in its utility; it is for this reason that they condemn such actions as the
Elevation of the Alms-dish so frequently
witnessed in our pure Protestant devotions,
declaring that it signifies nothing more
than the foolishness of the man who per-
forms the ceremony.

But I must confess that I think the
theory, so stated, somewhat misleading.
No doubt at the beginning it was as they
say.   The primitive clergyman who knocked
upon his breast did so because it was a
natural action for a gesture-loving South-
erner who wished to express his sorrow; the
unlettered deacon who requested a blessing
before reading the Gospel possibly desired
it to safeguard him in the face of the darkness of the catacombs and his own imperfect
education; even the Bishop who put on his

mitre may have done so for fear of a
draught. All that I maintain is that these
things are neither natural nor necessary
in modern well-lighted, well-ventilated
churches for clerics, who are sufficiently
educated not to stumble over the Latin,
and sufficiently self-restrained to repent of
their sins without striking themselves in
public. Yet these actions and others like
them are not only deliberately practised
but minutely regulated in the rubrics of the
most divinely human Institution on earth;
and it is surely far more illuminating to see
in this fact a sense that movement no less
than language may be the vehicle of internal intentions and external worship, than
to dismiss, with the scholars, the whole
matter as an utilitarian survival.

I remember being reproved as a boy for
indulging in gestures. I was told that the
modulations of the voice were sufficient for
any emotions proper to my age and condition; and that gesticulation was an evidence
of barbaric impulse. I resented the rebuke
at the time, and I resent it still; it appears

to me singularly unwarranted.   We have no more right to condemn the language of the hands and arms than the language of the tongue.   We are furnished by our Creator with all these members; we desire to express ourselves as forcibly as possible; and why in the world should we not do so by all the means at our command?

It is this, then, that the Catholic Church recognizes in her rubrics.

Neither can she be accused of inculcating formalism.   It is exactly as formal, neither more nor less, for one man to knock upon his breast when he is far from contrite, as for another to declare himself an erring and straying sheep when he is congratulating himself on his extraordinary probity (let us say) in his Saturday operations in the City. Both gesture and word may be formal, but neither need be.   Indeed, the Catholic Church is less liable to the charge than the Establishment; for it is perfectly recognized in the one that the priest is the representative not only of the congregation, but of the

entire Christian world, and stands where he
does in that capacity and in no other; while
in the other such views are denounced as
popish and unscriptural superstitions. The
one has her eyes on the whole body, the
other on the individual; the one, roughly
speaking, conceives of a religion as consisting in an objective piece of honour done to
God, the other as a subjective devotional
attitude of soul.

Catholic ceremonial, then, I maintain, is
far more than a way of doing things —
it is a thing in itself; and, again, roughly
speaking, Protestant ceremonial is the
reverse.

An instance or two, perhaps, may serve
to illustrate the difference.

A year or two ago it was declared by our
Archbishops at Lambeth that incense was
not recognized as part of the worship of
the Church of England; but upon being
pressed to consider Primitive Christianity,
they conceded that a purely fumigatory
use of the censer would not be considered
disloyal. Now, the Catholic does not use

incense that he may smell it, but, to employ
a straightforward Scriptural phrase, that
God may do so.

Lights upon the Holy Table, again, in
the Chancellor's phrase, are not permitted
"except when required for the purpose of
giving light." To whom? Obviously to
the clergyman, and to no other; for the
Edwardine symbolism, referring to the sig-
nification of the Light of the World, has
been expunged from the Book of Common
Prayer: not even the congregation is considered.

Ceremonial, therefore, for the Protestant
is a way of doing things; for the Catholic
it is an offering that he makes to God together with incense, candle-wax, and such
things. His movements, his bows, the carriage of the hands, his knocking upon the
breast, his osculations — all, in fact, which
is summed up by the urbane and amiable
Protestant as his "bowings and scrapings"
— are not necessarily the expression of his
own emotion, nor of that of the possibly dis-
tracted congregation which observes them

— they are neither more nor less than
official actions done before God's majesty as
a means of confessing what is due to Him,
and obtaining from Him what is desired.

With this in mind, then, observe once
more with me the motions of those three
men in green at the foot of that lighted,
fragrant altar, and see how orderly and
exquisite is the whole affair. It is no less
than a sacred dance, and there is hardly
one religious emotion that does not find
its representative there.

First, then, the actors in this drama,
representing, let us say, a father and his
two sons, are so swathed as to present the
least possible resemblance to men. Their
humanity, their corporal defects or advantages, the lines of their bodies, even their
passions, their stupidities, their brilliancies,
— all are obliterated as far as possible beneath the stiff folds of an antique dress; for
they are not there as the Reverend Smith,
Jones, and Brown, but, as performers in a
stupendous drama, figures in a sacerdotal

act done primarily to God, and secondarily
with as little distraction as possible before
men.   They resemble giant images of which
the mechanism is studiously concealed.

The movement begins with an adoration
reduced to the lowest minimum of a descent
on to one knee, performed, I dare say,
sometimes with the nonchalance of a
courtier entering the first ante-room, but
not the less significant on that account.
Then, after a pause, Contrition makes her
appearance, bending as if to deprecate
wrath, striking her breast as if to chastise
the body.   Then, ascending, the choragus
kisses the place of sacrifice; and proceeds
with a swaying movement to and fro,
accompanied by his partners, to offer incense.

This surely is what we may call the
"first figure."   To and fro they go, the
children linked to their parent by a single
finger and thumb, to the chink of chains,
till the altar is encompassed by smoke;
and I must confess that the result of this

on the beholder is to put him curiously in tune with the spirit of worship. Mystery, awe, expectation, a chastened familiarity, a sense of rhythm and order and seemliness, such as befits the initiated Christian in the presence of His Fatherly Majesty — of all these emotions I am conscious as I look from my pew in the distant nave. God remains God to me; He is not degraded in my eyes to the proportions of "an immeasurable clergyman," to the fashion in which I am compelled to think of Him when at home I witness my estimable Rector stride up the steps, as if they belonged to him, bury his face and arms in a velvet cushion, and proceed to deliver the opening paragraphs of the Communion service with an air of never having seen it before.

Here, on the other hand, I am still able to think of my Maker as a Spirit who, since He has descended in human form and has reassumed that nature to His throne, must be approached through actions apparent to the senses, yet stiffened by the

remoteness of His Splendour into a kind
of Court etiquette.

The second figure begins by a gathering
of the three performers round the illumi-
nated book, suggesting to me the inadequacy
of a single man, however highly consecrated,
to approach his God. His companions,
like Aaron and Hur, stand about him and
help him to utter the formula of "entering
in," and the ninefold cry for mercy as the
glory becomes visible through the far-
distant, open door. The cluster breaks,
for order must be observed, and reassured
the three wheel about and come up to the
altar in line for the song of praise that is
God's due. And here it may be noted,
as a remarkable piece of liturgical insight,
that at every moment of poignancy during
the entire audience, the three stand together
in one line — when they cry glory to God
in the highest, when they protest their
loyalty, when they call him by His supreme
name and make one with the ushers of
His Court, when they entreat mercy and

peace from the Lamb of God — at these occasions, and these only, are the three stiff figures in one horizontal line, as if need demanded that one man should not speak alone, as if enthusiasm or agony of desire propelled his supporters from their positions in the rear. They too must look upon God's face. Yet in all the set speeches, in the more formal addresses, when instances of the King's graciousness are solemnly quoted, and He receives the formal homage due to His threefold being, the assistants are content to stand behind and observe the most precise rules of precedence.

The singing of the Epistle and Gospel are accompanied with peculiar rites; the subdeacon, like a child called suddenly to an important office, goes here and there as if excited: he clasps the precious book, is led by the prompter to make his bow, reads the words on a monotone, allowing his voice to crack upwards at the close; then he runs to his father as if to ask whether he has done it well, kisses his hand in a passion of pride and hears him say, "God bless you, my son." Then in a burst of enthusiasm he breaks the figure and runs across with the Gospel-book to the proper place.

But at his elder brother's singing of the Gospel, an astonishing elaborateness is observed. They go about here and there, lights are brought in, and blessings distributed. The youngest child is not allowed to touch the holy thing except in the capacity of a lectern. Incense is blessed, and the white pages are soaked in the sacred antiseptic, for fear that the eyes and lips of a mortal man might smirch the purity of the Incarnate Life which he proclaims. The father, too, faces about towards his eldest son, and obediently kisses the page which the imperious child points out to him — so imperious, so absorbed in his precious burden that he omits to make his reverence as he passes through the beam of light that pours downward from the Tabernacle.

At the Offertory, the harmony of movement is disturbed, for matters have to be arranged, and deacon and subdeacon become for the moment ordinary persons who hand about bread and wine and water, and make things ready. The youngest, too, is forced to stand aside for the present, and a mere man in a surplice takes his place to turn the pages; for to the boy is given an important duty. To him is committed the silver cradle in which the Body of the Prince is to lie presently; so he muffles his hands and the utensil all together in a cloth for fear that he should breathe upon it or touch it, and stands breathless down below while the other two go about their business on the highest step. He partakes of the character of a sentry, a servant, and an observer. He has nothing to say or do; he must stand perfectly still till he is wanted. He would give the world to go up and down again with the other two and the censer in that rhythmical dance with which the door of the second ante-room is approached; but it is not allowed him. He must comfort himself with reflecting on the high honour bestowed on him with the guardianship of the paten, and the pleasure of looking through the door.   His one relief is to step up for an instant for the *Sanctus* and return.

And now there is no movement.   The hierarch has wheeled on his heel and begged his assistant to pray for him; he has whispered his first sentence in the King's ear, a hint at the secret boon he will ask presently, and has then stepped back to make a cheerful noise to the God of his salvation. Then again he comes close for his long, mysterious colloquy.   He is explaining matters, with his hands now held out in entreaty, now brought together in a passionate clasp at the close of his sentences, as he names the Prince's name.   He refers, I learn from my book of words, to other eminent instances of His Majesty's clemency; and he winds up by an appeal that makes all sure.

Qui pridie. . . .

Then he bends very near indeed, all drop on their knees in astonishment at such condescension; he wipes his fingers with a nervous, hasty movement, and then the astounding event to which all has been tending takes place. A little bell rings, and he receives in his arms the Body of the Infant Prince for which he has been begging so long . . . just to hold Him, just to hold Him for a minute or two. . . .

Ah! was not the posturing and the drama and the runnings to and fro, and the tapping on closed doors, and the plucking of courtiers by the sleeve, and the whispered entreaties to be spoken for — was not all this worth it? For he holds now, at his mercy, the precious Person whom God loved so much, and whom yet for love of another He was willing to give to the shame and pain of the Cross. Is there anything on earth that His Majesty can refuse, now that He has given the most precious thing in Heaven? And is there any limit to what that priest can ask, who has asked so much and got it? Even to me, Protestant as I am, it did seem completely suitable that an event so stupendous could scarcely be approached by any other process than that of a sacred dramatic dance, with an accompaniment of rigid and minute Court etiquette. To leave the conduct of such a thing to the individual personality and the private taste of a simple clergyman in a surplice, would be nothing else than bathos of the worst description; human outlines must be obliterated by some overpowering uniform, personal tastes and methods of behaving must be rigidly supplanted by set movements and gestures.   In fact, for such a drama as this we need not clericalism, but the most emphatic sacerdotalism.   Originality in the sanctuary, as has been well observed, is the grossest vulgarity known to men.

The rest of the Mass followed the lines already indicated; but the movements were less elaborate, more confident — (no wonder!) — and slightly more human. The youngest son restores the paten presently, and takes off the silk cloth; he receives at the proper time the kiss of peace — that inexpressibly tender fragment from a simpler and more loving age — and in his turn

passes it on till it dies in a ripple of movement among those others who stand and
wait; later again he bows low, with his
brother on the other side, and, as his
supreme privilege, is permitted to take the
cover from off the Precious Blood. . . . Then
he finishes the wiping of the vessels which
his father has begun, puts them away, and
returns if he can to take part in the last
simple movement. There is less deliberation here, for the audience is at an end; so
he kneels with his brother to be blessed,
answers his father, shuts the book, and
comes down to form into line for the last
time. The three make another adoration
towards the palace-windows, and with the
crash of brass and wood and the shrilling
of strings, they join the deputation that has
accompanied them to the gates; and Mass
is done.

But how surprisingly graceful and eloquent the whole affair has been! Emotions
have been expressed in four or five lan-
guages simultaneously; by sound, colour,

smell, words, and movement. Could anything be more explicit, more likely to obtain
its object before God to whom all hearts
are open, more likely to save His worshippers from distraction? Of course each is
unnecessary regarded from one point of
view; some may be bewildering to an un-
instructed observer, and yet all should stand
or fall together, in spite of the privilege of
the sectarian to exclude any one of those
vehicles according to his private taste. The
Anglican repudiates the unknown tongue
in his worship of God, who, however, as a
seminary priest said on the scaffold, "well
understands it." The Baptist banishes
smell, and as far as possible, colour and
grace of movement; the Quaker refuses
these and the sound of words besides. But
the Catholic who aspires to count all men
as his brethren employs every vehicle that
his romantic brain can suggest: he batters
the Kingdom of Heaven by five portals at
once; he is not ashamed to take his place
with the worshippers of Isis and Cybele,
with King David, and with the naked

Fijean, and to dance with all his might before the Lord.

I must confess that I shall look with dismay upon my clergyman next Sunday. It is not that he does not dance, but that he has nothing to dance about, and has not learnt the steps. . . .

RELIGIOUS PERSECUTION

JULY, 1904.

MR. MARJORIBANKS will not let me be: he has been at me again, this time as to Popish persecutions, the massacre of St. Bartholomew, Torquemada, and Bloody Queen Mary. And I may as well confess at once that I could not answer him; I am well aware that there are answers — that the Huguenots were desperate conspirators, and that the Pope struck the medal, not in thanksgiving for their death, but for the news of the King's escape; that Torquemada's methods were mildness itself compared to those of the contemporary civil law of England, that Good Queen Bess stood a head and shoulders above her sister in truculence; but these answers do not content me. I am not willing to allow that the Catholic Church is only a good

deal better than everything else; she should
be surely quite different from all else: her
standard should be heavenly, not earthly;
her Law, the Sermon on the Mount rather
than the Napoleonic code.

When, therefore, the clergyman rhetori-
cally demanded whether my moral sense
was not as much outraged as his own
when I contemplated the disciples of Jesus
Christ using the stake and faggot for the
defence of the Gospel, I was obliged to
assent.

I have, however, been pondering the
question since, and I think that I have
been able to formulate a few conclusions
that were dark to me before.

Now, the root of the whole matter — the
reason of this complete reversal of public
opinion — seems to me to lie very deep, and
to be entwined with nothing less than our
conceptions of God's intentions for the
salvation of man.

The world has seen some very curious
variations in these conceptions. In the

middle ages it was commonly understood
that man was saved by faith and works —
by the response of his inner nature to God's
Spirit, and the coincidence of his outer
actions to God's Will. Luther stoutly pro-
tested against the second of these two
ideas: he declared that the attitude of the
soul was all that mattered; that the outward life was comparatively unimportant:
a man, he proclaimed, is saved by faith
without works. In our own days the pen-
dulum has swung completely across. A
man's faith, it is said, is comparatively
unimportant, it is his actions that matter.
The Catholic Church, on the other hand,
has remained motionless throughout: faith
and works, she declares, are alike necessary.
Not half, but the whole of man's nature
must co-operate.

It is useless to discuss whether she is
right or wrong; but that she has been
stable when all else has changed, is an
undeniable fact. She holds the positive
principles on either side, and always has so
held them.

Now, on these premisses I do not understand how religious persecution can be condemned by those who continue to support the framework of society by means of the hangman and the rope. Society, it is said, must be kept up at all costs; individual whims must subordinate themselves to the good of the community: I am not allowed to fire guns in the street, to throw stones at my neighbour's windows, to strangle Mr. Marjoribank's baby. In one sense I am free to do so; but if I do so I am fined, imprisoned, or hanged according to the nature of my crime. In other words, in the opinion of society, a man is justified or condemned by his works, not his faith.

If, however, it is once granted that justification by faith is also true, I do not see how we can object to the fires of Smithfield and Toledo, for exactly parallel arguments, neither more nor less, can be adduced in their behalf: and Beza, Luther, and Calvin were the first to say so, and even to act upon their theory.

When I strangle Master Marjoribanks I

commit at least two injuries: I kill the child, and I imperil society; — the harm inflicted on my own character is a negligible quantity. Very well, answers the world; you have chosen to do this, and therefore in self-defence I choose to hang you.

Now, when a man fell into heresy precisely the same argument was applied.

"You are endangering," cried Torquemada— "you are endangering the salvation of your neighbour, even if you have not already actually assaulted it; you are injuring the whole scheme of the Church by which salvation is to be found; and you have done more than this: you have insulted the Divine Majesty, and you are slaying your own soul. Therefore you will appear next Saturday in the market-square and be put to death there according to agreement."

Now, honestly I do not at first see how to answer the Spaniard except by denying his premisses — by crying out that a man is not justified by his faith, that it does not in the least matter what he believes because there

is no such thing as definite Revelation, by
joining myself with those who say that outward works are alone important, and that
the rest must be a matter of individual
choice.

It is of no use to tell him that his laws
were brutal: he will answer me that they
were far less brutal than the civil laws of
contemporary England, and that the State,
and not the Church, was responsible for the
penalty.   It is of no use to tell him that a
man's faith cannot be compelled at will: he
will answer me that it can; for that faith is
not an intellectual process or an emotional
state, but an act of the will assenting to the
Church, exactly as loyalty is an act of the
will assenting to the State.   And he will
add, moreover, a number of even more irre-
futable arguments. He will tell me that the
word "heresy," used in the sense of his time,
always and invariably denoted a spirit of
anarchical revolt which rebelled not only
against Revelation, but against both morality and civil authority as well; he will remind me that it was apostates, not infidels,

who suffered, and that the Church always
denounced in the fiercest manner any
attempt to proselytize the latter class by
any means but those of quiet persuasion;
and if, in a final struggle, I assert the rights
of conscience, he will ask me how far I am
willing to respect those rights in a man
whom conscience bids blow up Parliament-
house with gunpowder.

Where, then, lies the escape of one who
like myself regards a right faith as of equal
importance with a right life? Does it lie in
the retort that corporal penalties in such
matters are utterly alien to the gentle spirit
of Christ? I think not; for it would be
equally hard to show that Jesus Christ's
words are compatible with our own Worm-
wood Scrubs and Wandsworth gallows. So
long as we continue to enforce morality
and punish attempted suicide by such
matters as the Criminal Law Amendment
Act and the police-court, so long, indeed,
as we resist the evil-doer at all or summon
a policeman with his truncheon to resist him

on our behalf, so long will it be impossible to take the Sermon on the Mount in its literal sense; we must be content with some other interpretation of it before we can deduce that we are justified in using force against either violence, or immorality, or heresy in any shape or form.

The escape seems to me to lie in another direction.

So long as the Catholic Church was actually as well as ideally the undisputed mistress of the inner life, the whole framework of society, civil and moral alike, rested upon her as their sanction and support. All finally came back to her and to the laws that she proclaimed, and revolt against her supreme claim meant a blow struck against society as a whole. Under these circumstances, therefore, granted that the civil magistrates were justified in punishing theft, I do not see how it can be denied that Torquemada was justified in punishing heresy. (The Quaker argument I deeply respect, which is to the effect that both magistrate and inquisitor are alike wrong

— but I am not dealing with that: I am assuming that the Quaker is wrong.)   But, I repeat, if the magistrate is right, the inquisitor was right.   It was not a question of detail, but of principle; public opinion declared unhesitatingly that the constitution and inviolability of the Church were no less certain than the constitution and inviolability of the State. Religion in those days was neither more nor less a matter of opinion than loyalty is in our own; the average man was far more insulted by being called a heretic than our own citizens were insulted three years ago by being called pro-Boers.   To the simple eyes of Spaniards Christ's Revelation was as much assured to him as representative government or Magna Charta to ourselves.

But times have changed. Religion is now a matter of opinion, perhaps even of mere convention, amongst most of our civilized nations; it is impossible to say that public order and peace rest with us upon a revealed dogmatic basis. Society professedly protects, not the rights of God, but

her own; she punishes theft, but not forni-
cation; she avenges blasphemy, not as being
an insult to God, but an offence to her own
ears. It is utterly impossible, therefore — it
is more, it would be actually immoral — for
the Catholic Church to attempt to act according to her old methods. She would
now be protecting, not a universally
acknowledged fact, but a personal opinion.

This change, I suppose, took definite
shape in England towards the end of
Henry VIII.'s reign, and about the same
time began to affect the continent of Europe.
Mary Tudor, therefore, must be blamed, not
for tyranny, but stupidity; she had not
realized the momentous transformation, and
she attempted to act as if Protestantism
were a passing breeze, not a steady wind.
But for Elizabeth I can find no words too
hard; she was attacking, not a new opinion,
but the old faith; she used her rack and
knife against that which had secured to her
the throne, not against that which threat-
ened it; she punished men for standing
still, not for moving forward in a new and

dangerous direction; and, above all, she who now stands forth in the Protestant world as the champion of private judgment, racked and butchered those whose private judgment did not coincide with her own.

Mr. Marjoribanks, therefore, can take courage. He need fear neither for his flock, his baby, nor himself, when he contemplates such an improbable event as my turning Papist. I should not dream of gathering a company of masked familiars and surrounding his house at nightfall in an attempt to terrify or rack him in the direction of an act of faith; I should consider such an attempt as not only foolish, but actually immoral; for by such an act I should be defending, not the constitution of English or European society, but only what I should then believe to be God's Truth. And God's Truth, pure and simple, apart from its union with civil law (faith, that is, without works), can no more be propagated by ropes or whips than can a man's private opinion on lust or truthfulness be affected by the same means.

Religious persecution, Mr. Marjoribanks, I repeat, is not an attempt, and never has been an attempt, to change a man's inner mind by means of direct pain, any more than the hanging of Mr. Palmer of Rugeley was an attempt to persuade him that the poisoning of his friend, Mr. Cook, was an immoral action. Certainly many heretics, possibly even Mr. Palmer himself, were led by the prospect of death to reconsider their position; but the main idea in both courses was primarily to protect that scheme in which men in general, it was believed, found their justification, and by which they lived. . . .

SCIENCE AND FAITH

JULY, 1904.

I HAVE lately emerged from a fit of gloom
— a fit that, I am beginning to see, recurs
as regularly as any other physical depression in those who are endowed with the
"artistic temperament." It is difficult to
put its characteristics into words; but I
think it will be useful for me to attempt it,
and to write down at the same time the
considerations which have helped to disperse its horror.

It was this: — It seemed to me that
Religion was a very unsatisfactory affair
altogether. Here we are, placed in a world
of undoubted matter — a world that, in
spite of philosophers, is a fairly intelligible
thing — intelligible, that is to say, as far as
action is concerned. If you will but be sensible, I told myself, and live an ordinary life,

and do things that please me, and relieve
suffering in others so soon as that suffering
becomes an unpleasant thought to myself,
and observe the ordinary social laws, and
look after myself, and give tit for tat — in
short, live exactly as nine out of any ten
men do live — life becomes a very reasonable and pleasant affair. For, after all,
does not religion give one more pain than
pleasure? It is for ever interfering with my
natural instincts, and perplexing me with
the additional problems of itself, and making demands for which apparently it gives
no adequate compensation. Further, it is
not as if religion was undoubtedly and irre-
futably true. If, of course, I knew for certain that God was God and the Catholic
Church His representative, I should be
simply a fool if I did not lead a religious
life; but I do not know it. Millions of
persons far more clever than myself deny
it; and, on the other hand, they put forward theories, supported it seems by science,
which certainly appear to explain everything with the exception, of course, of the

main primal mystery as to why anything is at all. There are vast countries on which Christianity has made no impression, there are other countries, and those highly civilized, where Christianity is fading. And, once more, is not Catholicism extremely improbable after all? It is based upon the belief that God became man — in itself highly improbable — and from that fact flow out with — I must confess — irresistible logic, a number of doctrines and theories that seem to me, when I am in this mood, the *reductio ad absurdum* of that Incarnation. Take the single doctrine of Transubstantiation, for instance — observe the Devotion of the Tabernacle. . . . There, in that iron safe, say the pious, in a silver cup made by Messrs. Jones and Willis, is the Eternal Incomprehensible God together with the Soul, the Body, and the Blood of One Who died nineteen hundred years ago, in an obscure Eastern province. Now, is that likely? . . . Certainly, say the real agnostics, it *may* be true, and the further side of the moon may be made of green cheese; but it is scarcely reasonable to ask us to sacrifice undoubtedly real pleasures, and to deny those senses by which we are in relations with the sensible world, and to upset our lives, and to devote hours of daylight to prayer, on the supposition that that improbable thing may possibly be a fact.

Ah, how convincing it all sounds when one is in the agnostic mood; and how incredibly mean and unconvincing when one is not!

Now, I cannot explain the mysterious movements of the soul by which I have emerged from that fit of depression; all I can do is to write down the outlines of a few considerations which floated on the surface of those movements.

The principal of them was the thought of the Transcendence of God.

It is quite certain that if God exists at all, He exists in a completely different manner from that in which we exist. Our first conceptions of Him, considered philosophically, must be of the negative order.

He is not as we are; He has not a mind like ours; He does not occupy space; He does not therefore move or change; He does not progress through time; yesterday, to-day, and to-morrow are obviously all one with Him.   In fact, of God as He must be in Himself, we can say very little except negations.   He is not here *and* there, then *and* now; He just is.

But then, on the other hand, we do and are these various things; and, intellectually, we cannot really picture to ourselves an existence in any other mode than ours, or argue about it.   When we think we have pictured a spirit, really all we have done is to think of a thin kind of body. . . . Therefore the gulf between us and God seems impassable.   His thoughts are not only higher, but they are actually other than ours in their very nature.

Now, the agnostic, and indeed a great many other people who would repudiate the name, are more or less content with that.   They shrug their shoulders — "Yes; if there is a God He is like that; then what

is the use of bothering? How on earth
can we know anything about Him? Meanwhile here is practical work to be done, and
mutton to be eaten, and women to be loved,
and books to be read and written, and
ordinary civilized life to be carried on; or,
if you want more, here is suffering that had
better be relieved, and social reforms that
might as well be inaugurated — all these
things rest on an intelligible basis: then
why fret about the Transcendent?"

But it seems to me that they omit a most
vital point. Granted all this, we have yet
to remember that on our assumption that
there is a Transcendent God, the world as
we know it came into being by Him; and
that therefore the gulf is not actually but
only intellectually impassable. Spirit did,
as a matter of fact, express itself in matter;
and further, therefore, it follows that there
is nothing more reasonable than to believe
that It should still communicate with us in
the same terms. What, then, follows from
this but that "Religion," although dealing
with and leading to Transcendence, must

be for all practical purposes in the same plane of existence as we, and not as God?

Now consider the Tabernacle again, or the Incarnation, for they are both the same — and are they so unreasonable? True, Messrs. Jones and Willis made the Ciborium, and pious nuns the bread; but what has that really got to do with it? If Transcendent God communicates with man — and it is really unthinkable that He should not — He is bound, not by His limitations, but by ours, to communicate with us through means that are as material as ourselves.

We see, then — or at least I do — that religion must, from our nature, be inadequate to the Divine Essence, simply because we are in one mode of existence and He is in another; but that does not at all mean that it is in the least untrue or inadequate to our needs.   We cannot help materializing everything, picturing spirit under a bodily image, conceiving of God as an old immeasurable man, and so forth; and therefore even revealed religion is bound to be of the same kind.   God, in other words, is bound

to use images and things that are within our
range.   To say that the Devotion of the
Tabernacle is limiting to spirit, is to imply
that it is unworthy of God to have made
matter, if it is unworthy of Him to use it.

The truth, then, lies in neither of the two
extremes of spiritualism and materialism —
neither in Mrs. Eddy nor Professor Huxley;
nor, again, in that vague invertebrate religion
(so dear to the British mind), always
oscillating between the two and faithful to
neither: but in a frank and full conception
of both. It is, of course, the tendency of the
religious mind to be exclusive — to dwell
either upon the Transcendence of God and
to sneer at the reality of sacraments and
creeds and the particular devotions of the
unthinking pious; or upon the material side
of religion, and to think that our necessarily
anthropomorphic images of the Deity are
adequate to His Nature and Being.   But
the truth surely lies in both.   God is Transcendent, therefore no dogma is adequate:
God communicates with man; therefore the
system of religion that comes from Him —

whatever that may be — is absolutely true
so far as it goes. The reasonable Catholic,
therefore, seems to me to have all the advantages of both sides. He has all the agnosticism of the agnostic with regard to God
as He is in Himself; he has all the fervent
faith of the Breton peasant in the local
manifestations of the supralocal, and the
verbal definitions of the Ineffable.

A second point flows naturally out of
this.

Intellect plainly is insufficient for religious
belief; but so it is also for every other branch
of knowledge except the exact sciences. The
exact sciences, we must remember, have, properly speaking, no real existence at all except
in man's brain; they are abstract, not con-
crete. There is no such thing, for example,
as "two" in the world, as Mr. Illingworth
says somewhere: "Two" is always united
(except in the brain, and perhaps even there
also) with apples or horses or persons. There
is no such thing as a line or a point or a
circle. These sciences, then, are literally the
only ones in which intellect is competent:

in history, geology, art, chemistry, and the rest, a thousand other faculties come in. A man must have predispositions, theories, observations, enthusiasm, faith in the word of others, if he is to make any progress in these other branches of knowledge. And yet, incredible as it may seem, apparently sensible persons demand that unless intellect be used alone in the realm of religion — religion, which is infinitely more complicated and exhaustive and inclusive than any other realm, since it embraces not only the entire life of man, but even the dealings of a Transcendent God and to some extent His Being — unless intellect is accepted as supreme, they will have nothing to do with it. Enthusiasm is blinding, they say (whereas really it is illuminating); predispositions are the parents of illusion (whereas really they are God-given aids to intuition); theories are full of bias (whereas progress is impossible without them); faith in the word of others is credulity (whereas really it is an exercise of the moral faculty). And so forth.

It is surely obvious then, to take yet one

more illustration, that religion cannot possibly be "proved." Only the exact sciences
can be "proved," in the sense in which that
word is commonly used. You cannot dem-
onstrate by chemical analysis the beauty
of a picture, or by reference to records the
atmosphere of fourteenth-century civiliza-
tion; by such methods no more can be done
than the handling of the grosser materials.
But the supreme judgment must be given,
not by this faculty or by that, but by the
entire man; his sympathy, his intuition, his
emotion, his self-knowledge, his experience
— not one must be wholly wanting; intellect by itself is powerless; there must
co-operate with it all that we mean by
character; and character, as we know, is
the result of living.

Turn, therefore, once more to religion.

Here is a subject which claims to concern
the whole of man, and more. It concerns,
first, man as he is in himself, his emotions,
his morals, his understanding, his thoughts,
words, and actions, his social relations, his
individual responsibility, his aspirations, his

doubts, his hopes; and, further, it claims to
concern all that God has done for him; his
creation, his redemption, his momentary
guidance and illumination.   If, then, one
single branch of man's activities — art or
historical learning — depends for its perfect
pursuit upon the entire man; if, for example, falling in love gives him new passion
in music-making, or a disappointment a
keen intuition into Napoleon's life at St.
Helena — how much more is every faculty
of his being, in short, his character as he
has made it out of his original nature by his
subsequent efforts and circumstances — how
much more is this to give evidence in his
supreme interest ?   An academic professor,
therefore, occupied with mathematics, is
open to the peril of one-sidedness; so is
the historian, the artist, the sensualist, the
philosopher; each in his own realm has
cultivated his faculties to an end unworthy
of their fullest exercise; he alone is supremely competent to judge of religion
who has dedicated his powers to its single
cause; who has tried to live, not to himself,

nor to any one branch of life exclusively, but to the study of the Will of God and to the manner in which He may be served.

"Thou hast hidden these things," cried Jesus Christ, "from the wise and prudent; and hast revealed them unto babes." . . . "Do the doctrine," He said again, "live the life, and you shall know the truth." . . .

Dear me! How plain it is just now! I seem to myself to have come up out of a small stuffy room on to the housetop. There I was last week, poking away among fossils and moths' wings and dust and confusion: my intuitions were as rusty tools; my emotions had ebbed; and above all, I was complacently regarding myself. And therefore Christianity seemed to me quite impossible. I was bothered by the Higher Criticism and the geological discoveries of somebody whose name I now forget. And now I have come up; and God's sky is over me, and the breeze is in my face. . . .

It is not that my intellect — such as it is — has ceased to work; on the contrary, it is working better than ever. I see all that

I saw last week; I remember everything except the name of the geological professor; I am capable this moment of delivering a short disquisition on the authorship of Isaiah; but, thank God, those other frailties are awake as well; my whole character — a poor thing, but all that I have got — is alive again; and I could sooner doubt of my own existence than of the Sacrament of the Altar or the Fructiferous Incarnation of the Son of God. . . .

LOW MASS

SEPTEMBER, 1904.

I MUST be frank with myself.

It is useless to pretend that I am not trying to make the best of the Roman Church; and, after all, I do not want to pretend otherwise, for the only conceivable way of understanding anything is understanding it; in other words, if you would judge of a system you must approach it as a friend, and not an enemy.

Now, it is as perfectly easy to pick holes in the manner in which Low Mass is celebrated, as to do the same office for Morning Prayer. If the one is mumbled, the other is preached; if the one is sacerdotal, the other is clerical; and both alike may be called by their respective foes an insult to man's intelligence. But it appears to me, in the enthusiasm of this moment, that

153

the former is at least not an insult to God Almighty's intelligence as well. It is not hinted that the Creator cannot understand the silent motions of the heart, nor be moved by a formal address unless it is delivered with skilful enunciation. Roughly speaking, then, it appears to me that the presence of God, who is a Spirit, is assumed as a matter of course by the Massing-priest, and loudly declared by the minister of the Establishment.

Two days ago I arrived in town by the early Irish mail at St. Pancras Station, and had an hour or two to spend at Victoria before catching the 9.15 for Little Brasted. So, after bestowing my luggage and breakfasting in the refreshment-room, I went for a walk. I have no sense of geography, and have not the faintest idea as to what the little church was into which I turned a few minutes before seven o'clock. It stood in a by-lane somewhere to the north of Victoria Street.

I suppose there were half a dozen people

there when I entered, and twice as many again when I went out half an hour later. There was a heavy fog outside and a fair sample of it inside, and the gas-lights at the back of the church had a kind of frosted halo, very pleasant to see, around their flames. The rest of the church was tolerably dark, except at the altar, where three candles burned, one at either end, and a third by the book on the right-hand side.

There was a dirty statue of the Redeemer in red close beside me against a pillar, with a guttered candle or two at the foot. There was a hideous round-topped red window cutting the gloom like a bloated moon overhead; and a very tawdry display of brass things, and what I took to be sham roses above the altar. It is impossible to describe how every artistic nerve in my body and soul was outraged. I began to wish I had gone to Westminster Cathedral instead, if I wanted piety, for there at least things are far enough away to look respectable.

Presently a small creature in white and black emerged from somewhere, snuffing loudly, and a fat clergyman came after, in the same sort of costume, only in his case the black was uppermost and the white beneath, and he wore an inelegant hat on his head, resembling that of a cook. The two approached the altar and went down, each on one knee; then the fat man, who had got rid of his hat, went up the steps and set some things down upon the table.

Then I made a great effort, and exhorted myself in somewhat of this fashion: "You have no business to say this kind of thing. After all, who are you? You are a broken-down actor of no fortune and no particular gifts. You have lived an irreligious life for the most part, and are only just now beginning to attend to the affairs of your soul. What do you know about religion, and of the way in which God wants to be worshipped? How do you know He doesn't prefer this kind of thing? Just attend and hold your tongue. Besides, you are extremely tired and cross with your night-journey: you are conscious of grimy cuffs and a crumpled collar and the absence of your usual bath. But for all that, try to behave decently inside as well as outside. Don't criticize. But attend, and try to conceive it possible that there may be something more in this world than your vast intelligence has already comprehended."

It did me a great deal of good; and by the time that the fat man had found his place and come down the steps again, I was in a more chastened mood. I was even willing to allow that he might know more about his business than I.

Well, I need not describe Low Mass at length. It is perfectly familiar to most people. But perhaps it is necessary to remark that it is not at all like High Mass. There is no posturing or singing; everything is done in an extremely business-like way, and as rapidly as possible. (I am even given to understand that some priests say what is called a *black Mass* as often as they are allowed, because it occupies ten minutes less than any other form of that service.)

The man appeared to say his piece, sometimes to himself altogether, and sometimes in a grumbling, discontented voice; and, for one of his condition, he moved almost briskly, washing his hands, and bowing down, turning the pages, and doing this and that as expeditiously as possible. A small' bell rang now and again; and the snuffling creature who attended the priest sneezed four times loudly in the dead silence, yet went about his work without a sign of disconcertedness. Finally, after a loud bawling on the knees, to which the small congregation responded as hastily as their choragus, the undignified procession of two shuffled away and disappeared. Then I took my hat and umbrella and went out too.

I must confess that I was very much astonished and disappointed at first as I groped my way in the fog. This was not like the Requiem; there was not an attempt to impress the audience even with the most sombre emotions; the whole affair was shabby and perfunctory. There was none of that glamour — of which I had heard so much; no mysterious hieratical figure performing functions which made the skin prickle to look upon; no awe, no incense, no earnestness. It was exactly such an entertainment as those described in a certain sort of tract, where a superstitious and blinded laity bow down before a series of actions that are as unintelligible to them as they are dishonouring to God. Surely, I said to myself, my own bright church at home, all alive with a gay altar-cloth and flowers, inspired by my dignified rector, who moves and speaks with such assurance, thrilled by the singing of ladies in a gallery, lighted by brilliant brass coronæ that, to sentimental eyes, resemble gigantic celestial crowns, — surely the clean pews, the white stone pillars, the rich organ, the thoughtful preaching, the incomparable English delivered with such fire, the thronging well-dressed congregation on Sunday mornings — in fact the whole affair — is infinitely more in accord with what we understand by Christianity, than this shabby, heartless, dingy, cold, formal set of actions that is called Low Mass.

Such were my reflections. And I cannot tell you when the change came; I suppose it was gradual. I began to conceive of another interpretation as I dozed in my carriage on the way down from Victoria; it had almost become outlined by the time that I reached home; and now that I have had a couple of nights' rest, and am sitting at my table, I think I understand a little better what it was all about.

First, then, it appears to me that the object of Low Mass, if I may say so, is God, not man. I do not say that Almighty God is not pleased with music and beauty and cleanliness: no doubt He is; but these accessories are not essential. I prefer my friend to wear a clean shirt, but he does not cease to be my friend when he arrives at my house after a night-journey. "Near is his shirt, but nearer is his skin"; and, I suppose, nearest of all his immortal soul. Something then in Low Mass is done towards God; I

confess I do not yet properly understand
what that is; but at least it is believed that
that is the object. Certainly nothing that
can be perceived by the senses is done
towards man, except what tends to repel
him. The fat clergyman turned his back on
the people most of the time — I am sure that
they could not tell, except from their books,
what he was doing up there; not one
word could be heard by them, except once
when I thought he said *Dōscum;* and therefore I presume that he was not seeking to
address them particularly; he wore shabby
clothes, the candles were not at all pretty,
nor the surroundings calculated to impress
the eye except with feelings of dislike.

Yet it seems to me that that point I have
mentioned is a very important one. If God
Almighty is really there, and desires to be
served by man, it is surely not vital, though
it may be more decent, to use stately and
magnificent ceremonial. The fact that
High Mass forms part of the Church's
offering, as I have tried to say in another
paper, shows that the Papists do not depre-

ciate good manners in approaching the
Divine Majesty; while Low Mass proves
that they do not consider etiquette essential.
(It is like a child who now calls his father
"Sir," and stands up in his presence, and
now climbs on to his knee and pulls his
beard or dozes with his head on the paternal
shoulder. I have no child, but if God had
given me one, I must confess that I should
have wished him to use both sorts of courtesy to me.)

Now at Morning Prayer God is undoubtedly present, because He is every-
where; but it is extremely hard to picture
Him as anything but a mere spectator,
diffused pleasantly through the sunlit
church, as is that faint odour of furs and
flowers and woodwork to be perceived
there on Sunday morning. He is a spectator, interested and satisfied perhaps, but
no more than that: He is not the object
of the worship in the same sense as at this
dingy little service I have described. Rather,
to my mind, He resembles a King, before whom his subjects, so engrossed in the

sweep of their trains, the carriage of their
swords and hats, and the correct enunciation of their protestations of loyalty, forget
the object for which they have come, and
whisper and bow, as in a ballroom empty
of a throne.

But at Low Mass there is another spirit
altogether. It is like the entering of a
small deputation at early morning, a little
frowsy perhaps and slovenly, but right into
the King's bed-chamber to assist him to
rise. It does not stir their emotions, as
when, with clash of brass and thunder of
drums and shouting of the populace in
brave array, they pace before him across
the Cathedral Square; but, for that very
reason, there is the less danger of their
forgetting for what purpose they do their
service. They are there to help the King
to get up, to pour water with chilly fingers,
to hand stockings, to light fires, to draw
curtains. There is no kind of fear that they
will do it for fun; they do it only because
he is the King, and they are his servants.

Now, I have already said that I do not

properly understand what service it was
that the man in black and white, with his
assistant, believed he was doing for God
Almighty; but I am quite sure that the
Lord appreciated his efforts, and the more
so because it was done so bravely and from
such a plain sense of duty.

Those people, too, who knelt behind me
and kept so deathly still — surely they were
not doing it for their own enjoyment either!
They were there because their King liked
them to be there, and they came even although they were not compelled, or even
attracted by the sensible beauty and dignity
of their service.

Was the devotional spirit, then, wholly
absent? I do not believe it, though I felt
none myself. And this brings me to the
second lesson I have learned from Low
Mass.

According to the Papist theory (and it
seems to me highly reasonable) there are
two elements of spiritual action to be considered. There is, first, what the Church,

in her official capacity, does for and on behalf of the individual; and there is, secondly, what the individual does on behalf of himself and of the Church to which he belongs. We may name these elements, for brevity's sake, the official and the personal.

Now, the official element finds its illustrations in a thousand matters, beginning with the Sacrifice on Calvary. This was done for all men, and a vast store of grace liberated for their benefit. The Church adds to this her official acts — what she calls her Merits; with her sacrifices, prayers, penances, and good actions. Every Contemplative House, according to this view, carries on, in union with the Life of God on earth, the work begun by that Life and Death. We might imagine it all as a vast manufactory of grace.

But the personal element consists partly in efforts not only to aid in the work, but to appropriate the benefits of it all to the worker. For example, if I were a Catholic, and from proper motives gave half a crown to a beggar, or said some prayers with sincerity, I should by a single action benefit the beggar, the Church, and myself, as well as please God.

These two elements, then, I take it, must always be kept in mind when we consider the Papist system, for it is founded largely upon them.

Now, I have never before realized in all my life what a simple illustration of the theory is presented in Low Mass; and it is rendered the more simple by the stripping from its presentation of all emotional accessories that might otherwise obscure it.

There at the altar stands the Church, in vestments proper to her mind at the moment, and she goes about her business in a business-like manner. She is not exhorting men, she is dealing with their Maker. She scarcely casts one backward glance, for it is wholly unessential to the effect of this particular business as to whether at the instant they are attending or not; it is all a much greater matter than that.

There behind kneels the individual —

(and I may here digress to bestow a maxim upon other Protestants, who, like myself, may sometimes attend Papist functions and tell them that when they are in doubt, to kneel, and remain kneeling). There, then, he kneels, a personal character with particular tendencies, likes and repulsions, objects, desires, ambitions, fears; and he is encouraged to retain them all so far as they will pass the test of God's fire. He is not, at this moment, being put through his exercises, or compelled to say these words and not those, to make postures, to generate prescribed emotions; he is left entirely alone; his minister is careful not to disturb him by talk, or movement, or exhortation; nor is he particularly encouraged to attend to what the clergyman is saying. He may do precisely what he likes, tell beads, read a meditation, or engage, if he is able, in mental prayer; in fact, he may follow whatever course he thinks best for the preservation of a suitable attitude of soul in the presence of the Divine.

Now, is not this an extraordinarily good

arrangement? Contrast with any other
system that you like. The Church of
England in her offices is a sour school-
mistress by the side of this Mother: her
pupils must kneel, pray, aspire, repent,
attend, hope, intercede, all to order. They
must rejoice in the *Venite*, meditate in the
psalms, praise in this canticle, bless in
another, listen to the tales of bloody-minded
kings who died thirty centuries ago, wrestle
with St. Paul's logic, or have the open eye
with John, and there is no appeal, or relief,
or concession. The Dissenters are yet more
stern, for these allow one uninspired man
to conduct the exercises according to the
state of mind he chances to be in, and lead
the dismal band with his arbitrary *bâton* in
strains that they have never practised. The
Quakers, indeed, attract one more than
either, for these at least leave a man for
the most part to his own moods, but they
lack the objective might of the Mass
enacted before the eyes, to remind us that
heaven-gate is open, God's eye observant,
and His Heart overflowing — even, if the

theory is true, to open His Heart yet more widely, and take the Kingdom of Heaven by the only force that Omnipotence cannot resist.

There then, if I had had eyes to see, was the entire Church of God at her official prayers: the white Carthusians were there, and the black Benedictines; the Poor Clares offered their blood and tears, and the Crutched Friars their liberty. Cries went up in that silence from India, France, and Greenland, for each altar is at the centre of the earth, they tell us; Mary was there, with her virginal eyes and mother's love; the black Jesuits, who struggled in Elizabeth's rope, were free to remind their God of their pain; not one was missing of all who ever cried upon Him in bliss, expectation, or the darkness of this world. For Jesus Christ their Prince was there, with broken Body, and streaming Blood, in whom each song was made perfect and each life accepted.

And there knelt I, free to play now this

note, now that, as my will dictated, in that
orchestra of glory; or to listen, or to regret,
or to aspire as I was capable.   And all that
I thought of was the fat man that I saw,
and the pinched creature that I heard
snuffling and ringing his bell; and the poor
candles, and the bloated moon of a window,
and the sham flowers!

But then, is it all true? . . .

BENEDICTION

NOVEMBER, 1904.

YESTERDAY afternoon, as it was darkening
to dusk, I stepped into the Catholic church,
and found a service in progress.

It was an astonishingly simple one.

Father Thorpe had set up above the altar
a large, flat, gilt vessel with a glass centre,
in the midst of which could be seen the
white disc of the consecrated Host; and
about it burned a dozen candles. There
was a boy or two on the altar steps, and
a number of children in the body of the
church who were singing a hymn on their
knees, while the clergyman swung a censer
two or three times before handing it back
to his companion.

Then there followed a Litany to Mary
the Mother of Jesus, and a collect; then
another hymn and another collect; after

171

which the priest went round behind the altar, took down the monstrance, and, carrying it to the front, made a large sign of the cross with it over the congregation. Then he replaced, as I suppose, the consecrated Host within the tabernacle while the congregation sang a short psalm; and the service was over.

I was so much interested and surprised that I made an opportunity to inquire of the sacristan what it was that I had witnessed, and, from his explanations, and a hymn-book that he allowed me to borrow, I think I have by now tolerably understood the meaning of the very simple ceremonies of the afternoon.

Briefly, the whole affair rested, as so many other functions of the Catholic Church, upon her belief that the consecrated Host really and truly is the Body of Jesus Christ.

It is of no kind of use to attempt to understand or even to criticize effectively this service of Benediction, as it is called, unless one first takes for granted this faith

in the Sacrament. Without that faith, all
is indeed superstitious and meaningless;
with it, it becomes intelligible and natural.

The idea, I imagine, is something as
follows.

When a soul approaches her Creator, she
does so in order both to give and to get;
to praise Him and to pray to Him. In
Mass, a sacrifice is offered, and the etiquette, therefore, is somewhat formal and
stiff; a liturgical form is found to be both
suitable and instructive. But Almighty God
is not only infinitely far, He is also infinitely
near; He is not only complex in His operations and attributes, but He is simple in
His nature — and this, I suppose, is what
Christ meant to teach us when He said that
God was Love, that He was our Father,
that He was Light, and so forth.

Now, all this is acknowledged, and indeed
insisted upon, by the Protestant, who has
a clearer view of God's love than of His
majesty, of His simplicity than His com-
plexity. We are told at Exeter Hall that
we need no churches nor images nor cere-

monial, that God is a spirit, that a gathering round the family coffee-pot may be as pleasing to Him as the most gorgeous procession, terrible with banners; and in one sense, of course, I fully agree with the rhetorician. I take it that the Christian Revelation proves to us that we have access to the Father; that mental prayer may reach His throne no less surely than plainsong; that God, who is simple, likes His children to be simple too.

Well, Benediction seems to show to me that the Catholic Church fully recognizes these facts. It is true that she believes what the Protestant rejects, namely, that the Sacrament is really and truly the Body of Christ, but this belief illustrates to my mind her superior simplicity of attitude: her doctrine of the Real Presence in itself is not the climax of an elaborate logical process — the elaborateness of her exposition of it was only forced out of her by the elaborateness of the attack — in its essence it is merely an entirely simple acceptance of the words of her Master, "This is My

Body": she accepts neither more nor less than the bare meaning of the words as they stand. It is His Body, she says; and since He is alive, where His Body is, He is. Therefore the Sacrament is Jesus Christ, and must be treated like Jesus Christ.

In Benediction, then, she acts upon her faith with an extreme directness. The Real Presence is a mystery, of course, as regards its mode, but no mystery as regards its fact — or rather it is one of those mysteries that it is her ceaseless business to disclose. God is there, and must be treated as God; therefore she takes the three symbols — music, lights, and incense — those three symbols that man has somehow always associated with divine worship, and employs them in her devotion: moreover, she aims them directly at that holy thing which she declares to be God; she addresses Jesus Christ as the Salutary Host, she sends up her fragrant smoke immediately before the monstrance, she burns her candles immediately round it. Finally, at the very end,

her priest speaks no word; he must not
come between God and the souls of His
children; therefore he envelops his hands
in a cloth, and in dead silence permits
Jesus Christ to use him almost mechanically
in the Divine bestowal of the blessing of
peace. He lifts and moves the Sacred
Host in the form of a great cross, but he
is silent; Another is speaking soundless
words in his stead.

Let us have done, then, with this Protestant claim to simplicity. Compared
with the elaborate doctrines of Anglican
and Nonconformist divines — their safe-
guardings, their hesitations, their agnosti-
cisms, their refusals to define, their volumes
of negation and warning, — the Catholic
faith is as a naked statue set by the side
of an elaborately costumed wax-work
figure. Mr. Marjoribanks once told me
that the Anglican doctrine of the Eucharist
would occupy a couple of hours for its
adequate statement; Father Thorpe told
me that the Catholic doctrine can be stated

in four words, and those Christ's HOC
EST CORPUS MEUM. Compare again,
let us say, Evening Prayer with Benediction; and it is a fair comparison, for each
alike is at the present day the normal service of Sunday evening, each in its respective communion. The one is an extremely
beautiful and scholarly composition, drawn,
it is true, almost entirely from Catholic
Vespers and Compline, but can it be compared for simplicity and direct appeal to
the ignorant and heavy-laden, with that
amazingly plain and moving ceremony
which I have described? I do not say
that Evening Prayer is not admirable for
the learned and devout, just as Vespers
among the Papists is extremely suitable
for monks and holy persons, and as it was
once suitable even for the masses when
they understood what it was all about and
were able to answer the priest intelligently.
But in our own days, when the cry for
simplicity and Gospel teaching and Jesus
Only is waxing louder and louder among
those who are in the least interested in

Christianity, and when a total lack of interest in both faith and morals is becoming more and more evident among the rest, can it be denied that Benediction seems almost to have been inspired from Heaven, to combine directness of appeal, easiness of comprehension, and proclamation of the central doctrine of the Catholic creed, all in one unliturgical quarter of an hour? It comprises the unformality of general hymn-singing without its purposelessness, the freedom of the prayer-meeting without its wild undogmatism, the eloquence of the preacher without the distraction of his personality, the impressiveness of sacerdotalism freed from the clerical element. It demands no vivid sense of the omnipresence of God, for there He is within that little white circle; no high spiritual soarings, for He is not a hundred yards away; no straining of the eyes in the realm of faith, for here He is all but in sight.

Now, I am aware that there are a hundred

retorts available; and the first, that in fact which Mr. Marjoribanks has stated more than once with his usual fervour, is that the whole affair is grossly materialistic.

I do not propose to answer this at any length; but I will content myself with asserting once more that it is neither his business nor mine to find fault with God's methods when once it is clear that they are His methods. I do not wish to entangle myself in Anglican subtleties; I will only say that if it is really true that the Sacrament is Christ's Body, I cannot understand how it can be materialistic to treat it as such; or if it is materialistic (though I shrewdly suspect that my friend does not realize the meaning of the word), then it is right to be materialistic because God Almighty wishes us to be so. The whole thing stands and falls by the reality of the Presence.

But the Vicar of St. Symphorosa would chime in here.

"My dear sir," he would say, "it is useless to talk like that. I am as firm a

believer in the Real Presence as yourself;
but I would not dream of treating the Holy
Sacrament with such offensive familiarity.
Christ ordained it for the offering of the
Holy Sacrifice and the Communion of His
Body and Blood, and we have no right to
use it for any other purpose — and as a
proof of this I would remind you of the
fact that Benediction was an unknown
service in the early Church, that it was not
introduced into England until after the
Reformation, and that the Eastern Churches
to this day know it not."

Now, this objection appears to me far
more worthy of an answer than Mr. Marjoribanks'; yet I do not intend to answer
it at length, or to plunge into deep contro-
versy.   I will only say this.

I distrust the appeal to the early Church
with all my heart.   It appears to me, when
I hear it from the mouth of Anglicans, to
be always accompanied by a sense that the
Church of God is a kind of antiquarian
institution whose business it is to attempt
to reproduce in modern times a state of

things from which we have been purposely
delivered by Almighty God. We might as
well insist upon carpeting our floor with
rushes, and deprecating the use of forks,
because the Elizabethans had a better taste
in domestic architecture than ourselves.
There is no harm, of course, in such fads,
if we take them up merely as pastimes and
pretences; but they become fanatical nonsense so soon as they are seriously assumed.
To my eyes, God is the God of the living,
not of the dead; it is He who has made us,
and we must not try to unmake ourselves;
it is He who has substituted wheels for
rollers, steamships for barges, forks for
fingers, the electric telegraph for mounted
couriers.   His idea surely remains the same
throughout, that we should live our life, go
on journeys by land and sea, eat our food,
and hold communion with one another; and
He supplies means after means, now more
simple, now more complicated — the pen-
dulum of discovery continually swings from
side to side; a new force is unearthed, new
machinery springs into complex existence,

and presently subsides again into simplicity
— and all the while the business of life goes
forward swifter and swifter towards its
final consummation.

Now, why, in His Name, should the business of worship alone stand still? Why
should not new methods be continually
devised, elaborated, simplified, and even
superseded, so long as the principle remains
the same — the faith once delivered to the
Saints? Father Thorpe, as he lifted the
monstrance in silence, meant precisely what
St. Paul meant as he lifted the tiny white
fragment from the cracked plate in the
upper room at Ephesus, crying, "The Body
of the Lord broken for you!" Each alike
honoured God, declared the Faith, and
desired that through that Living Bread
the people might be succoured.

What business has this clergyman to
protest and criticize? Let him rather look
to himself that in rejecting life and develop-
ment he may not be rejecting the Lord of
them both; that in his zeal for English anti-
quarianism he may not be faithless to Him

before whom there is neither Jew nor Greek, bond nor free; that in his anxiety to be faithful to ancient practice he may not betray Him who is unchanging in a thousand forms and under ten thousand symbols, Jesus Christ, the same yesterday, to-day, and for ever.

Such, then, are my first impressions of Benediction. It is true that possibly after a while I might find it wearisome; but I do not think I could find it wearisome if I loved Jesus Christ, and believed that He was really there. A child who climbs on his mother's knee night after night with the same words, or a boy who is blessed every night by his father and told to be good, can scarcely find these ceremonies tiresome unless there is some shadow between him and his parents. Therefore, if I should find myself wearied of the perpetual *Tantum ergo* and *Adoremus in aeternum*, I should look for the reason, not in those pulsating songs of joy, but in my own cold heart: I should ask myself, as in fact I do, whether I truly believe that Jesus Christ is really present, and whether I do find Him fairer than the children of men.

Yes, these questions are the important ones to ask. We want no philosophical or antiquarian discussions. . . .

THE PERSONALITY OF THE CHURCH

November, 1904.

I DO not propose to be so foolish as to attempt to define what I mean by Personality, nor even to describe it at any length. It is not the resultant of innumerable living cells in union, nor the sum of intellectual and emotional qualities, nor is it even identical with Character. It is partly these, no doubt, and may be viewed, or even sometimes stated, in the terms of each of these three systems, yet it transcends them all. It may be compared, perhaps, by an amateur such as myself, most luminously, to a chord of music, — "not a fourth sound, but a star." Like the flame of fire, the fragrance of a rose, the glory of a sunset, it may be analyzed and accounted for

by the philosopher or the chemist, but
it can be apprehended only by the poet,
artist, or lover.   So at least it seems to
me.

The point, however, which I wish to
discuss with myself is the fact of the personality, or at least something resembling
it, of which we are aware in every society,
divine or human.   Just as the personality
of a man transcends the sum of his attributes, or appears to do so — for a character
may be attractive to me, who dislike every
one of its component elements so far as I
know them — so the personality of a society
may be something very different from
what one would conceive to be the aggregate of those personalities which compose
it.   It is a notorious fact, for example,
that a company consisting of pleasant,
right-minded folk is often found in its
public acts to show neither courtesy nor
conscience: a board of ten directors may
cheerfully pursue a career of social crime
which would be the horror of each of its

members; a college may be composed of twelve tolerant scholars, and yet in its policy afford a shocking picture of narrow-minded and ungenerous bigotry.

Yet the explanation of this is not far to seek; it is to be found in the fact that in all human societies the bond of union is not one of courtesy or conscience, still less of immortal souls: it is rather for commerce or learning, or some other mutual material advantage that they combine. A director of a railroad may be a church-warden or a mystic, but he is not united with his fellows in that capacity; and the result, therefore, of Monday morning deliberations is what might be expected of a number of persons who have officially left their Christianity at home. The religion, and even the motives that guide each gentle-man in his domestic dealings, are wholly absent, not indeed from him, but from the contribution that he makes to the business for whose sake he is seated at the green-covered table.

Instances might be indefinitely multiplied

of this curious social fact. A mob collectively may be swayed by motives which each howling unit would unhesitatingly repudiate; a jury may, after an hour's deliberation, condemn a fellow-creature to death on evidence which each juryman would scarcely think sufficient to turn the balance in the buying of a horse; and yet, who can doubt that trial by jury is, on the whole, supremely just? The fact remains, explain as we will, that when once a union is set up between sentient wills there comes into being a strange character — I had almost called it Personality — which appears at any rate certainly transcendent of, and even alien to, the various elements of which it ought to be the result.

If this thought is a significant one, when we consider its bearing on human societies, how far more pregnant it becomes when we transfer it to that astonishing society which we call the Catholic Church. In that Church we have a union based, not upon commercial considerations, or the pursuit of science, but upon huge and monstrous facts which we are scarcely able even to apprehend. The souls of men are concerned, united one to another, not for temporal ends, but eternal. They are brought together, not for purposes of pressing earthly claims or conducting worldly business, or even advocating a certain system of thought, but that they may minister to the infinite glory of God and find a spiritual salvation which cannot even be pictured to the imagination. Again, the units which compose this society are selected on account, not of their capacity, but their needs; no nation or class is excluded; the saint has no more claim than the sinner, the theologian than the dunce. None are rejected save those who reject; none are encouraged save those who voluntarily correspond. Yet, with all this, if the Church's claim is true, the union that binds her children together transcends that of all human societies, as her object transcends theirs. The contribution that each must make is not that of one set of faculties, of this or that hour of time, of this piece of experience or that intention; but of his whole self, body, mind, and immortal soul; and each such self is welded into union with its fellows after a fashion for which there is no adequate analogy in the world. It is through a new and mystical birth that each must pass — a birth that changes character while it does not obliterate characteristics; and it is through this very birth, in the presence of which even the professed theologian is apt to doubt his powers, that every soul enters into a mysterious life flowing from God and permeating, not earth alone, but Heaven and Purgatory as well, which is named the Communion of Saints.

Again, approaching the subject from the dogmatic standpoint, we find a number of phrases in the Scriptures descriptive of this extraordinary fact, which appear to open to believers new ranges of thought as to its contents — Christ compares Himself to a Vine, of which His disciples are the branches, and seems, by the metaphor, to insist yet more strongly on the actually

Divine nature of His Church's personality. From one point of view the Church is composed of its members, from another it is identical with Himself. In one phrase we are informed that He is the Head and we the members, and in another that the Body, too, is His, indwelt by His Spirit and guided by His Mind. In brief, if we accept the New Testament as an authoritative · guide, we are informed that, while our instincts are right in attributing some kind of personality or character to every society, however loosely held together, the personality of the Divine Society which is called the Church is infinitely more worthy of the name, for that by virtue of the mystical union of all believers, or perhaps in response to it, there comes down upon it that transcendent personality from which all others flow, even that Divine character which is the possession of God alone. If a board of directors or a college of scholars generates a character alien from its component elements so far as we know them, the Catholic Church, on the other hand, generates a thing that on one hand we may call the Communion of Saints, and on the other the Spirit or the Mind, or even the Person of Jesus Christ Himself.

Now I am not the man to pursue this line of thought further; perhaps I am not even the man to pursue it so far; but it appears to me to illuminate a large number of dark subjects.   Let me mention two.

(1.) The act of faith, to one who can accept my presentation, appears no longer to be an unreasonable thing, for its object is no longer an elaborate system of thought which the convert is required to criticize, but a personal character.   Few men are capable, if indeed any are, of passing final judgment upon a philosophy or an art; but no man is excusable if he refuses to judge of one who claims his friendship: in fact, he cannot refuse, when once the claim is made clear.

I have no right to say dogmatically that

I know that homœopathy is a delusion,
unless I have made an exhaustive study of
its contents, and perhaps not even then;
but I have a perfect right to say that I will
choose this doctor and not that: and this,
I think, is a fair though rough parallel to
the search after religious truth. The Church
comes to me, not under the guise of a creed,
but in the habiliments of a person. "Look
well at me," she says, "read my history if
you will, ask for my testimonials, study
what I have to say; but, above all, give
me a personal interview. Exercise that
faculty which you exercise in the choice of
a wife, or a doctor, or a friend, and act
upon it. You may reject me as many others
have done and will do to the end of time.
Men make mistakes with the best intentions in the world, such as the conscientious
Pharisee or the distraught sinner made
when they looked upon Jesus Christ and
passed by. I do not even say that it will
necessarily be your fault; it may well be
that education, or prejudice, or natural
blindness, will lead even you to misread my

eyes; but do not make the mistake of thinking that your judgment is a matter only of
learning or profound study: it is not chiefly
that; it is a personal thing within the range
of all normal persons. I am not merely
the aggregate of my members, or the total
of my units. You need not know my history, or have precise knowledge of my doctrine, or estimate the statistics of the world's
morality. I am a kind of person, like
yourself, and I desire to be so treated."

(2.) The claim to infallibility, too, looked
at in the light of this supposition, is no
longer an absurd thing. It is said, sometimes with a show of reason, that the
judgment of a body of persons acting in
concert cannot exceed in value the judgment of all those persons acting separately.
So Fulke said to Campion. Yet we have
seen, even in human societies, how widely
such judgments may differ. The decision
of a jury may be something very different
from the aggregate of the opinions of its
members, since each may be dull and yet

all shrewd. How much more, then, may
not the judgment of a Divine Society,
united by a mystical bond of which we can
scarcely do more than guess the nature,
transcend the judgment of each of its members mechanically added together? And
above all, in view of the phrases which I
have quoted, it surely should not be hard
for those who accept Jesus Christ as God,
to allow that the judgment of His Church,
which in one aspect is indistinguishable
from Himself, is as infallible as His own!
Each reason, each quotation, each illustration of an Ecumenical Decree, may be faulty,
yet the decision itself be true.

Lastly, it cannot be denied that the
Catholic Church, at any rate, seems to present the phenomenon of a personal character quite unlike that of any other society.
She is accused by her enemies of being at
once unchanging and changeable, obstinate,
and capricious. She appeals to the imagination and the heart at least as much as to
the critical faculty. Men fall in love with

her, as they do not fall in love with the
Royal Geographical Society; she does not
depend upon her material accessories — she
is loved or loathed as much beneath a cor-
rugated tin roof as beneath fretted vaults
and spires; coarse boors and unemotional
peasants die for her as cheerfully as refined
scholars and attenuated mystics live by her.
And, on the other hand, her enemies hate
her with a passion that can only be personal,
they witness to her life by the very fury
with which they attack it.   In other words,
she presents exactly those phenomena which
surround a lovable person whose character
is sufficiently magnetic to affect all who
come within her range with either adoration
or hatred.   Above all she is credited, even
by those who deny her claims, with endow-
ments that can only properly belong to a
sentient being; she never forgets, it is
said, she plots, she welcomes, she inspires.
Mr. Mallock, in a moving paragraph or two,
describes her claim to have been present at
the empty tomb of her Lord and Spouse,
and explains that her children believe in

the Resurrection, not because of document-
ary evidence, but because of her word
who was an eye-witness of that supreme
credential of hers and His.   "I saw it," she
cries; "I witnessed the meeting of His
Mother and mine; I was in the boat with
John and Peter; I stood within the upper
room when the doors were shut; I watched
the cloud receive Him: I saw — I who
speak with you now."

Yes, there is no question about it that
if ever I find myself able to receive Christianity as Divine, I shall seek it at the mouth
of one who can vouch for its truth, and in
whose trustworthiness I myself believe.
Documents and criticism are not founda-
tions on which spiritual life, self-sacrifice,
and eternal issues can be safely reposed;
I have neither time nor power to sift evidence and weigh testimonies, nor sufficient
self-confidence to reject this as an accretion
and accept that as a survival.   I must put
myself, if ever I feel personally justified in
doing so, in the hands of one whom I per-

ceive to be Divine, whose life is as continuous as the centuries, whose memory
is as unfailing as time, and through whose
glowing eyes I see the Spirit of God to
shine. . . .

DEATH

January, 1905.

THIS morning my landlord ran into my room in great agitation, telling me that his cousin, who lived a hundred yards away, had been seized with some kind of convulsions and lay dying. The doctor had been sent for, and the priest — for the man was a Catholic; but neither was yet come, and the women were terrified.

I took my hat and ran back with him, and on the very doorstep encountered the doctor; and we went upstairs together.

The sick man had been got to bed, and lay there deathly pale, with open eyes, staring out senselessly through the window opposite, which none had thought to screen: his hands were hidden, his lips were parted, and his face twitched from time to time. A woman stood by him, helpless and anxious, nearly as pale as he; she gave a great sob of relief as we came in together.

While the doctor was at his work, I went and stood by the window looking out, wondering at the swiftness with which tragedy had suddenly dropped upon the sordid house. I wondered, too, as to a great many other things — as to the man's mind as he stared into eternity, the horror of the whole affair, the Supreme Mind which, apparently, plans such an exit from this life, and gives us all an hour of terror to which we must look forward. Why, too, I asked myself, is all so elaborate; why do we all do our utmost to prolong a life such as this, which has crept along suffering from internal pain, as I knew, for more than ten years? And my answer was that it was instinct, not reason, that inspired us; death was so shocking that there was no question but that it must be resisted with might and main as by a kind of reflex action: our efforts were scarcely defensible, but entirely necessary and natural. I thought this, and a great deal more, as I looked out on to the woods in the valley beneath. It was a windless morning, mellow and sweet; the ground fell away rapidly below, and the meadow merged presently in a slope of undergrowth that rose up into saplings and birches, and deep woods beyond. The air was like warm wine this morning, soft and invigorating: over the leafless branches there lay a velvet softness as of coming spring, and over all rose up the tender vault of blue skeined with clouds.

I must confess that it was chiefly ironical horror that prevailed in my mind. It was terrible to think that a Lord of Love was supposed to be transcendent beyond that sky and immanent in this lower air and life — a Lord of Love that was Almighty, too, and could so easily have arranged all otherwise, or explained it a little to reassure us that there was some plan behind this apparent carelessness and brutality. Here was a chess-board of black and white — of suffering and sweetness, the dying man and the kindling woods; and what right have I to choose to say that the board is essentially

white and only accidentally black? If it
were I who were dying, should I not feel
that agony was the truth of it all, and
peace no more than an occasional incident?
So far as I remember pain, it seems to me
to be so.

This Lord of Love, too — what was He
doing at this time, and His Mother and the
saints and the hosts of impassible spirits?
Were they aware of what was happening?
They watch and give no sign, and the
horror goes on, ruthless and inevitable.

When I turned round at a sound, Father
Thorpe was at the doorway.

Now I cannot describe, except very
briefly, what took place next, for I am
quite unskilful in ecclesiastical matters and
should no doubt blunder.

First of all, the priest came across to the
table near me, drew out a little bag, all
without a word, set down two doll's candles
and lighted them.   He spread a little linen
square, put up a little crucifix; and then
drew from round his neck another bag with

cords. He opened this, and set down a tiny silver thing like a watch.

Then I saw that the others were kneeling, and I knelt down too.

Presently, he was across again by the bed, kneeling by it, and telling the sick man that he was come to give him the Last Sacraments. He said that Jesus Christ had died on the Cross for his sake; that God did not ask us to do what we could not, and that He understood that confession was impossible. He must make an act of contrition, then; let him say in his heart, "My God, I am sorry for my sins because I love Thee with my whole heart."

He spoke like this for a moment or two, with a kind of brisk, but not untender, earnestness, looking steadily at the white face that stared back at him with scarcely more than a glimmer of sense; then he stood up, and pronounced, I suppose, the Absolution. Then he was back again at the table, opening the silver watch-case.

I did not like to observe very closely; but

I was aware presently that the priest was
holding up the little white disc and repeating some words: then he was back again at
the bedside, leaning over the dying man, and
there was something resembling a tiny
struggle, as the man was heaved up by his
cousin and the priest bent forward. . . .

Then the anointing began; his hands, his
eyes, his ears, his nostrils, and his mouth.
All, one by one, were signed by the priest's
thumb; finally, the bed-clothes, already
loosened, were drawn up at the end of the
bed, and his feet, too, were signed and
covered again.

Then, after a few more prayers and ceremonies, to which I did not attend very
closely, the priest blew out the candles and
went out of the room to whisper with the
doctor.

Now, written down badly like this, I am
aware that all this sounds most unimpres-
sive, distinctly "vain," and probably rather
superstitious. Yet all that I can say is that
these ceremonies and words, the bearing

of the priest, the half-intelligent response of the sick man, who was by now clasping a crucifix and looking upon it, the sudden frozen stillness of those who assisted — in fact, the effect of the entire performance — produced an extraordinary change in me.

As I sit now in the evening writing this in my study, it appears to me that my first reflections on the tragedy and heartlessness of death were those of a stupid savage. I cannot tell what it was exactly that wrought the change; I can only say that when all was done, the change was there.

Death no longer seemed to me a sickening horror; it had turned into a warm and soothing presence; it was awful still, but with the mysterious awfulness of a great and quiet forest rather than that of a slaughter-house or a wind-swept icy peak with howling precipices. It was as if, after a couple of harsh notes had been struck on some instrument — notes of brutal irreconcilable contrasts, another had been added to them which resulted in a solemn sweet chord. There was no longer that shocking

inconsistency between the mellow day outside and the death-sweat and mortal pains
within; it was no longer true that a Lord
of Love held Himself apart in some sunny
Heaven and tossed this heart-breaking
problem down into a venomously cruel
world; it was all one now: He held both
in the hollow of His Arms against His
quiet Heart, in a span so vast that I could
not follow it, but in an embrace so warm
that I was no longer chilled.

Ah! it is not possible to say how all this
came about, nor how real it was to me.   I
can only tell myself again that it was like
a chord of music, struck without a stroke,
sounding without vibration, welling out in
the stillness as of an orchestra of strings
and mellow horns held long to one great
harmony that reconciled good and evil,
pain and joy, life and death, God and
nature.

I do not think that I am either heartless
or sentimental.   I know that there were
tears on my face just now as I was told
that the sick man died an hour ago, and I

do not think that they would have been
there if he had died in my presence before
the coming of the priest. It was that
which resolved the discord and made me
understand — that series of actions and
incomprehensible words; the sense beneath
them all that told me that God cared and
had provided, and that if He allowed the
death, He furnished strength to meet it.
Without that I should have been hard and
resentful and agonized; with it I was able
to weep instead.

What a religion this is in which to
die!

I wish that I could explain all that I
mean by that, or even the effect upon me
of what I witnessed. Those ceremonies
were as the sliding of a key into an intricate
lock; we cannot grasp the mysteries of the
words, yet the door is open and we can
look within for a few minutes. We cannot
even remember or tell what it is that we
have seen. I cannot even tell myself what
I saw there, except that it was not a black

and empty room into which I looked.
Death is not like that; it is sweet and
friendly, as a fire-lit hall into which men
may see from the darkness outside.   There
are, too, no doubt, other doors through
which we may look; but I am sure that
the same view is not seen through these.
That is the least of what I mean when
I say that this is the religion in which
to die.

The first paper of this kind which I ever
wrote was, I remember, on the Requiem on
All Souls' day; and here I am back again
at the same heart-shaking point, death, and
what is behind death, and beneath it, and,
above all, supreme over it.   I wonder, as I
sit here and write, whether this is possibly
the conclusion of my circle; whether I have
been led from death to death, as from
strength to strength, looking at this and
that, and making my poor little comments
and drawing my cheap conclusions, and
airing my sickly sentiment or my distressing
humour?   After all it does not matter very
much.   No man can do more than is in his

power, as Father Thorpe said this morning,
and though I am well aware of my own
sublime inadequacy, there is this one hole
into which I can creep from the wrath of
the Lamb, and that is my own sorrow that
I have ever offended Him. . . .

Yes: this is a religion in which it is
possible to die properly. What else but
this would have served that unimaginative,
middle-aged man whom I saw alive eight
hours ago? He did not want sentiment,
or exhortations to an emotion of which he
was incapable, or adulation from friends
who seek to make death easy by an insin-
cere flattery of a life that was far from
stainless. He did not even want appoint-
ments to be made with Him in Heaven,
reminders that they would all meet, good,
bad, and indifferent alike, at the foot of an
improbable throne. He wanted a great
deal more than that, and a great deal less.

He was a sinner, and he knew it, and he
wished to be dealt with on that understanding. He wished to be as clean as
possible, and so he was absolved; to be

accompanied by God on that mysterious journey, and so he received *Viaticum*; to be strengthened and cleansed once more, so he was anointed; to escape — as was but natural — all pains that could be avoided, and so he received the Last Blessing. Finally, he wished to have his failing eyes cheered, and his nerveless hands supported, so the image of his Saviour was put into his grasp.

We have lived so long by our senses, counting that real which we can touch and handle, that God in His mercy allows us in all reality to do so to the end. He takes oil and bread and water and metal, and makes them, not only the symbols, but the very vehicles of what we require. "Look on that," cries the Church, as she holds up her crucifix, "there is the image of your Lord; kiss it for His sake. Look on this," as she lifts the Host, "This is He Himself — *Ecce Agnus Dei!* Taste and see that He is gracious. . . . Turn your hands over and feel the soft oil. . . . That is His mighty loving-kindness. Abandon yourself to these things; throw your weight on them, and they will bear you up. Seize them, and you have hold on eternal life."

Please God, that she may say these things to me! . . .

THE END